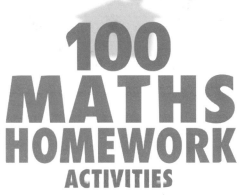

100 MATHS HOMEWORK ACTIVITIES

CONTENTS

GW00535847

Published by
Scholastic Ltd,
Villiers House,
Clarendon Avenue,
Leamington Spa,
Warwickshire CV32 5PR

© Scholastic Ltd 2001
Text © Wally Nickels and
Jean Livingstone 2001
Additional material on pages 6–8
© Ann Montague-Smith 2001
1 2 3 4 5 6 7 8 9 1 2 3 4 5 6 7 8 9 0

AUTHORS
Wally Nickels and Jean Livingstone

EDITORIAL & DESIGN
Crystal Presentations Ltd

COVER DESIGN
Joy Monkhouse

ILLUSTRATORS
Ray and Corinne Burrows

Acknowledgements
The publishers wish to thank:
Ann Montague-Smith for her invaluable advice in
the development of this series.
The Controller of HMSO and the DfEE for the use
of extracts from *The National Numeracy Strategy:
Framework for Teaching Mathematics* © March 1999,
Crown Copyright (1999, DfEE, Her Majesty's
Stationery Office).

British Library Cataloguing-in-Publication Data

A catalogue record of this book is available from the British
Library.

ISBN 0-439-01849-8

PAGE IN THIS BOOK	100 MATHS HOMEWORK ACTIVITIES YEAR 6		NATIONAL NUMERACY STRATEGY		100 MATHS LESSONS		
	ACTIVITY NAME	HOMEWORK	STRAND	TOPIC	NNS UNIT	LESSON	PAGE
29	Up to a million	Practice exercise	Numbers and the number system	Place value	①	①	⑰ ⑱
30	Investigating really large numbers	Investigation	Numbers and the number system	Place value	①	②	⑱ ⑲
31	Crossing the river	Games and puzzles	Calculations	Understanding x and ÷	② ③	①	㉒ ㉓
32	Estimate!	Maths to share	Calculations	Understanding x and ÷	② ③	②	㉓ ㉔
33	Using grids to multiply	Practice exercise	Calculations	Mental calculations x and ÷	② ③	④	㉔ ㉕
34	Cross-number	Games and puzzles	Calculations	Paper and pencil x and ÷	② ③	⑤	㉕ ㉖
35	Divisions	Timed practice exercise	Calculations	Paper and pencil x and ÷	② ③	⑦	㉗ ㉘
36	Problems	Practice exercise	Solving problems	Number problems in 'real life'	② ③	⑨	㉘ ㉙
37	Fractions everywhere	Games and puzzles	Numbers and the number system	Fractions	④ ⑤	①	㉞ ㉟
38	Broadacres Primary	Investigation	Numbers and the number system	Fractions	④ ⑤	③	㊱
39	Danehurst Road	Practice exercise	Numbers and the number system	Ratio and proportion	④ ⑤	④	㊲ ㊳
40	Karen and Rachael's money	Practice exercise	Numbers and the number system	Ratio and proportion	④ ⑤	⑤	㊳ ㊴
41	Over, under and between	Practice exercise	Numbers and the number system	Decimals and percentages	④ ⑤	⑧	㊶ ㊷
42	Stop the clock fractions	Timed practice exercise	Numbers and the number system	Decimals and percentages	④ ⑤	⑧	㊶ ㊷
43	One to fifty	Investigation	Numbers and the number system	Decimals and percentages	④ ⑤	⑨	㊷ ㊸
44	Paris	Investigation	Handling data	Handling data	⑥	①	㊼ ㊽
45	Touring Paris	Practice exercise	Handling data	Handling data	⑥	②	㊽ ㊾
46	Fun Run	Practice exercise	Handling data	Handling data	⑥	④ ⑤	㊿ 51
47	What are the chances?	Investigation	Handling data	Handling data	⑥	⑥	51 52
48	Know your cars	Investigation	Handling data	Handling data	⑥	⑧	52 53
49	Estimating angles	Timed practice exercise	Measures, shape and space	Shape and space	⑧ ⑩	①	61 62
50	Measure and calculate	Practice exercise	Measures, shape and space	Shape and space	⑧ ⑩	③	63
51	Making triangles	Investigation	Measures, shape and space	Shape and space	⑧ ⑩	④ ⑤	63 64
52	I'm thinking of...	Maths to share	Measures, shape and space	Shape and space	⑧ ⑩	⑥	65
53	Cubes again	Games and puzzles	Measures, shape and space	Shape and space	⑧ ⑩	⑨	67

PAGE IN THIS BOOK	100 MATHS HOMEWORK ACTIVITIES YEAR 6		NATIONAL NUMERACY STRATEGY		100 MATHS LESSONS		
	ACTIVITY NAME	HOMEWORK	STRAND	TOPIC	NNS UNIT	LESSON	PAGE
54	Perimeters and formulae	Practice exercise	Measures, shape and space	Measures	8 / 10	11	68 / 69
55	Measurements everywhere	Investigation	Measures, shape and space	Measures	8 / 10	14 / 15	70 / 71
56	Find the partner	Games and puzzles	Solving problems	Making decisions	11	1	78
57	Walk the tightrope	Maths to share	Calculations	Mental calculations + and –	11	2	79
58	Decicalc additions	Practice exercise	Calculations	Paper and pencil + and –	11	3	80
59	Decicalc subtractions	Practice exercise	Calculations	Paper and pencil + and –	11	4	81
60	Square number challenge	Timed practice exercise	Numbers and the number system	Number properties	12	1	85 / 86
61	Sequences and term numbers	Investigation	Numbers and the number system	Number sequences	12	2	86 / 87
62	Pascal's Triangle	Investigation	Solving problems	Reasoning about numbers	12	3	87 / 88
63	About how many?	Investigation	Solving problems	Number problems in 'real life'	1	1	95 / 96
64	Goals!	Maths to share	Numbers and the number system	Number sequences	1	2	96 / 97
65	Find the clues	Games and puzzles	Calculations	Paper and pencil x and ÷	2 / 3	1 / 2	100 / 101
66	First to the top	Maths to share	Calculations	Mental calculations x and ÷	2 / 3	3	101
67	Decorating	Practice exercise	Solving problems	Number problems in money	2 / 3	4	102
68	Multiplications	Timed practice exercise	Calculations	Paper and pencil x and ÷	2 / 3	5 / 6	102 / 103
69	Find the function	Games and puzzles	Calculations	Paper and pencil x and ÷	2 / 3	7	103 / 104
70	Decimal divisions	Timed practice exercise	Calculations	Paper and pencil x and ÷	2 / 3	8 / 9	104 / 105
71	Cash and Carry	Practice exercise	Solving problems	Number problems in 'real life'	2 / 3	10	105 / 106
72	Tinscombe town survey	Practice exercise	Numbers and the number system	Fractions	4	1	111
73	Round up or down?	Practice exercise	Numbers and the number system	Decimals and percentages	4	2	111 / 112
74	Low to high and round about	Practice exercise	Numbers and the number system	Fractions	4	3	112 / 113
75	Connections	Practice exercise	Numbers and the number system	Decimals and percentages	4	4	113 / 114
76	Polyhedra	Investigation	Solving problems	Reasoning about shapes	5	1	117
77	Pentagons from circles	Practice exercise	Measures, shape and space	Shape and space	5	2	118
78	Straws and pipe-cleaners	Maths to share	Solving problems	Reasoning about shapes	5	3	118 / 119

	100 MATHS HOMEWORK ACTIVITIES YEAR 6		NATIONAL NUMERACY STRATEGY		100 MATHS LESSONS		
PAGE IN THIS BOOK	ACTIVITY NAME	HOMEWORK	STRAND	TOPIC	NNS UNIT	LESSON	PAGE
79	Shapes using co-ordinates	Practice exercise	Measures, shape and space	Shape and space	5	5	120
80	Co-ordinates – reflections	Practice exercise	Measures, shape and space	Shape and space	5	6	120 121
81	Where's the shape?	Practice exercise	Measures, shape and space	Shape and space	5	7 8	121 122
82	Areas everywhere	Maths to share	Measures, shape and space	Measures	7 8	1	130 131
83	Puzzling shapes	Games and puzzles	Measures, shape and space	Measures	7 8	2	131 132
84	Which way?	Investigation	Measures, shape and space	Measures	7 8	4 5	133 134
85	Pinball	Practice exercise	Handling data	Handling data	7 8	6	134 135
86	Computer vouchers	Practice exercise	Handling data	Handling data	7 8	7	135 136
87	Pulse rates	Investigation	Handling data	Handling data	7 8	8 9	136 137
88	Guess the graph	Investigation	Handling data	Handling data	7 8	10	137 138
89	Repeat it	Games and puzzles	Numbers and the number system	Number sequences	9 10	1 2	143 144
90	Function fun	Maths to share	Solving problems	Generalising about numbers	9 10	3 4	144 145
91	Target practice	Practice exercise	Calculations	Mental calculations + and –	9 10	5 6	145 146
92	Midworthy School's Easter Fayre	Practice exercise	Solving problems	Number problems in money	9 10	7	146 147
93	Conversions	Practice exercise	Solving problems	Number problems in measures	9 10	8	147 148
94	Foreign currency	Practice exercise	Solving problems	Number problems in money	9 10	9 10	148 149
95	Factors and primes	Investigation	Numbers and the number system	Number properties	11	1 2	152 154
96	Factorising and prime factors	Practice exercise	Numbers and the number system	Number properties	11	3	154
97	Big wheel	Games and puzzles	Numbers and the number system	Number properties	11	4 5	155 156
98	Pathways	Games and puzzles	Numbers and the number system	Place value	1	1	163 164
99	Make it real	Practice exercise	Numbers and the number system	Ordering and rounding	1	2 3	164 165
100	Multi-hex	Practice exercise	Calculations	Paper and pencil x and ÷	2 3	1 2	169 170
101	What's the cost?	Practice exercise	Solving problems	Number problems in money	2 3	3 4	170 171
102	Timed divisions	Timed practice exercise	Calculations	Paper and pencil x and ÷	2 3	5 6	171 172
103	Exploring numbers	Investigation	Solving problems	Reasoning about numbers	2 3	8 9	173

PAGE IN THIS BOOK	100 MATHS HOMEWORK ACTIVITIES YEAR 6		NATIONAL NUMERACY STRATEGY		100 MATHS LESSONS		
	ACTIVITY NAME	HOMEWORK	STRAND	TOPIC	NNS UNIT	LESSON	PAGE
104	Getting close	Timed practice exercise	Calculations	Mental calculations x and ÷	② ③	⑩	⑰④
105	Mixed and matched	Practice exercise	Numbers and the number system	Fractions	④ ⑤	①	⑰⑦ ⑰⑧
106	Triangular growth	Practice exercise	Numbers and the number system	Ratio and proportion	④ ⑤	③	⑰⑨ ⑱⓪
107	Using percentage	Practice exercise	Numbers and the number system	Decimals and percentages	④ ⑤	④ ⑤	⑱⓪ ⑱①
108	Timing TV	Investigation	Numbers and the number system	Decimals and percentages	④ ⑤	⑥	⑱① ⑱②
109	Netball results	Practice exercise	Numbers and the number system	Decimals and percentages	④ ⑤	⑦ ⑧	⑱② ⑱③
110	Decigrid	Games and puzzles	Numbers and the number system	Decimals and percentages	④ ⑤	⑨ ⑩	⑱③ ⑱④
111	Stepping stones again	Investigation	Handling data	Handling data	⑥	① ②	⑱⑥ ⑱⑦
112	Graphs from ordered pairs	Practice exercise	Handling data	Handling data	⑥	③ ④	⑱⑦ ⑱⑧
113	Name that graph!	Practice exercise	Handling data	Handling data	⑥	⑦ ⑧	⑱⑨ ⑲⓪
114	Find the triangles	Games and puzzles	Solving problems	Reasoning about shapes	⑧ ⑩	① ②	⑲⑦ ⑲⑧
115	Where is it now?	Practice exercise	Measures, shape and space	Shape and space	⑧ ⑩	③④ ⑤	⑲⑧ ⑲⑨
116	Following instructions	Practice exercise	Measures, shape and space	Shape and space	⑧ ⑩	⑥	⑲⑨ ②⓪⓪
117	How does it get there?	Practice exercise	Measures, shape and space	Shape and space	⑧ ⑩	⑦ ⑧	②⓪⓪ ②⓪①
118	Counting diagonals	Investigation	Solving problems	Reasoning about shapes	⑧ ⑩	⑨ ⑩	②⓪① ②⓪②
119	Tug o' war	Practice exercise	Measures, shape and space	Measures	⑧ ⑩	⑪ ⑫	②⓪② ②⓪④
120	Cora's 100cm² puzzle	Games and puzzles	Measures, shape and space	Measures	⑧ ⑩	⑬	②⓪④ ②⓪⑤
121	Around the world	Maths to share	Measures, shape and space	Measures	⑧ ⑩	⑮	②⓪⑥
122	Converting measures	Practice exercise	Solving problems	Number problems in money	⑪	①	②⓪⑨ ②①⓪
123	Target basketball	Games and puzzles	Calculations	Mental calculations + and −	⑪	②	②①⓪ ②①①
124	Trouble-shooting	Practice exercise	Solving problems	Number problems in money	⑪	③	②①① ②①②
125	Crack it!	Games and puzzles	Solving problems	Making decisions	⑪	③ ⑤	②①② ②①③
126	Multiple problems	Practice exercise	Numbers and the number system	Number properties	⑫	①	②①⑥ ②①⑦
127	What can you say?	Investigation	Numbers and the number system	Number properties	⑫	② ③	②①⑧ ②①⑨
128	What's the difference?	Investigation	Numbers and the number system	Number properties	⑫	④	②①⑨ ②②⓪

100 MATHS HOMEWORK ACTIVITIES

100 Maths Homework Activities is a series of teachers' resource books for Years 1–6. Each book is year specific and provides a core of homework activities for mathematics within the guidelines for the National Numeracy Strategy in England. The content of these activities is also appropriate for and adaptable to the requirements of Primary 1–7 in Scottish schools.

Each book offers three terms of homework activities, matched to the termly planning in the National Numeracy Strategy *Framework for Teaching Mathematics* for that year. In schools in England which decide not to adopt the National Numeracy Strategy or for schools elsewhere in the UK, the objectives, approaches and lesson contexts will still be familiar and valuable. However, you will need to choose from the activities to match your own requirements and planning.

These books are intended as a support for the teacher, school mathematics leader or trainee teacher in providing suitable homework activities. The series can be used alongside its companion series, *100 Maths Lessons and more*, or with any maths scheme of work, as the basis of planning homework activities throughout the school, in line with the school's homework policy. The resources can be used by teachers with single-aged classes, mixed-age classes, single- and mixed-ability groups, and for team planning of homework across a year or stage. You may also find the activities valuable for extension work in class or as additional assessment activities.

Using the books

The activities in this book for Year 6/Primary 6–7 classes have been planned to offer a range of mathematics activities for a child to carry out at home. Many of these are designed for sharing with a helper, who can be a parent, another adult member of the family, an older sibling or a neighbour. The activities include a variety of mental arithmetic games, puzzles and practical problem-solving investigations. There are also practice exercises, some 'against the clock', to keep arithmetic skills sharp. The activities have been chosen to ensure that each strand and topic of the National Numeracy Strategy *Framework for Teaching Mathematics* is included, and that the children have opportunities to develop their mental strategies, use paper and pencil methods appropriately, and use and apply their mathematics in solving problems.

Each of the 100 homework activities in this book comprises of a photocopiable page to copy and send home. Each sheet provides instructions for the child with a brief explanation of the activity for a helper stating simply and clearly its purpose and suggesting support and/or a further challenge to offer the child. The maths strand and topic addressed by each activity and the type of homework being offered are indicated on each page. The types are shown by the following symbols:

maths to share	games and puzzles	practice exercise	investigation	timed practice exercise

There is a supporting teacher's note for each activity. These notes include:

- **Learning outcome:** the specific learning objective of the homework (taken from the National Numeracy Strategy *Framework for Teaching Mathematics*);
- **Lesson context:** a brief description of the classroom experience recommended for the children prior to undertaking the homework activity;
- **Setting the homework:** advice on how to explain the work to the children and set it in context before it is taken home;
- **Back at school:** suggestions for how to respond to the returned homework, such as discussion with the children or specific advice on marking, as well as answers, where relevant.

Supporting your helpers

Extensive research by the IMPACT Project (based at the University of North London) has demonstrated how important parental involvement is to children's success in maths. A homework diary photocopiable sheet is provided on page 8 that can be sent home with the work. This sheet has room for records of four pieces of homework and can be kept in a file or multiple copies stapled together to make a longer-term homework record. For each activity, there is space to record the name of the activity and the date when it was sent home, and spaces for a brief comment from the helper, the child and the teacher on their responses to the work. The homework diary is intended to encourage home–school links, so that parents and carers know what is being taught in school and can make informed comments about their child's progress.

Name	JULIE SOAMES				
Name of activity & date sent home	Helper's comments	Child's comments			Teacher's comments
		Did you like this? Colour a face.	Write some comments on what you learned.		
CONVERTING MEASURES JUNE 7TH	Julie was interested and worked hard. She found the graph question difficult and so did I.	a lot 🙂 a little 😐 not much 🙁	WHEN WE DID THE CONVERSIONS AT SCHOOL I DIDN'T UNDERSTAND THEM VERY WELL BUT THIS HOMEWORK SHEET HAS HELPED.		I have spoken with Julie and cleared up some of her problems. If you would like a word about the graph pop in after school one day.

By the time children reach Year 6 some helpers will find the mathematics involved difficult. Clearly there is no simple solution, but involvement with the child in the activities may be helpful as will children explaining their methods. Teacher comments on helper's responses may result in opportunities to discuss the mathematics together at a convenient time. Furthermore, teacher/parent groups meeting to involve themselves in the mathematics and the teaching methods are invaluable.

Using the activities with 100 Maths Lessons series

The organization of the homework activities in this book matches the planning grids within *100 Maths Lessons: Year 6* (also written by Jean Livingstone and Wally Nickels and published by Scholastic), so that there is homework matching the learning outcomes covered in each unit of work in each term. Grids including details of which lessons in *100 Maths Lessons: Year 6* have associated homework activities in *100 Maths Homework Activities*, with the relevant page numbers, are provided on pages 2 to 5 in this book to help teachers using *100 Maths Lessons: Year 6* for planning.

About this book: Year 6/Primary 6–7

Running down the side of each homework page are statements indicating a single relevant strand and topic covered by the activity. However, the work in Year 6 often interrelates more than one strand or topic, and this should be borne in mind when selecting homework for the children. This book contains five types of homework activities, all recommended by the NNS for children in Year 6/Primary 6–7: 'Maths to share', 'Investigations', 'Games and puzzles' and 'Practice exercises', some 'Timed' against the clock. As this is the last year of homework in the primary school, children must have opportunities to work without the assistance of their helper. However, some 'Maths to share' activities still feature, while other types of activity encourage helpers to participate in particular ways. The 'Investigations' and 'Games and puzzles' involve practical investigations and problems often shared with a helper working with numbers, measures and shape and space, a mix of mental arithmetic and strategy games for two players and open-ended mathematical activities for a child to work on independently with appropriate guidance from a helper. The 'Practice exercises' provide children with opportunities for further practice of work done in school and include mental arithmetic to keep these skills sharp. These activities are designed for children to work independently at their own pace, or 'against the clock'. For these activities, helpers are given guidance on ways to help.

Year 6 SATs

The activities in this homework book are not designed to coach or otherwise prepare children for SATs specifically. The emphasis of the work in this book is to develop children's confidence and understanding of the different aspects of mathematics and to give opportunities for parents and children to share and enjoy doing different mathematical activities together. However, the emphasis on solving problems that is a feature of the activities will give confidence and facility with all aspects of mathematics and will inevitably support the children's performance in the tests.

Name _____

Name of activity & date sent home	Helper's comments	Child's comments		Teacher's comments
		Did you like this? Colour a face.	**Write some comments on what you learned.**	
		a lot :) / a little :| / not much :(		
		a lot :) / a little :| / not much :(		
		a lot :) / a little :| / not much :(		
		a lot :) / a little :| / not much :(		

Teachers' notes

TERM 1

p29 UP TO A MILLION
PRACTICE EXERCISE

Learning outcomes
- Read and write whole numbers in figures and words and know what each digit represents. (Year 5 revision)
- Order a set of integers less than 1 million. (Year 5 revision)
- Consolidate rounding an integer to the nearest 100 or 1 000.

Lesson context
Help the children to position numbers on a number line to 1 000 000 and conversely suggest which number 'lives' at a particular position on the line. Using a set of number cards, ask the children to place them in order and to give numbers which lie between any pair of the numbers. Round numbers to the nearest 100 or 1 000.

Setting the homework
Suggest that when tackling questions they may wish to jot down the steps on scrap paper.

Back at school
Mark the questions highlighting problems e.g. zero as a placeholder. **Answers: 1.** 86 542, eighty-six thousand, five hundred and forty-two; 24 568, twenty-four thousand, five hundred and sixty-eight, **2.** Nearer to 29 000; 170, **3a.** 2 070, **b.** 25 680, **c.** 730 096, **4a.** 499 800, **b.** 310 000, **c.** 875 000.

p30 INVESTIGATING REALLY LARGE NUMBERS
INVESTIGATION

Learning outcomes
- Read and write whole numbers in figures and words and know what each digit represents. (Year 5 revision)
- Consolidate rounding an integer to the nearest 10, 100 or 1 000.
- **Use appropriate operations to solve word problems involving numbers and quantities** based on 'real life' and money.
- Develop calculator skills and use a calculator effectively.

Lesson context
Encourage the children to provide estimates of large numbers and discuss estimation strategies, e.g. *How many words in this book?* Explore car prices or house price information in newspapers. Provide question sheets linked to the information, e.g. *Which new Toyota costs more than £13 000?*

Setting the homework
Explain the sheet, making sure that the children appreciate that they can use the question sheets linked to the information. They can, if they wish, choose their own ideas. Help less able children to focus on one of the ideas suggested.

Back at school
Review the children's responses, asking where their answers came from.
Answers: Various. Note: the total population of North America depends on the countries included. Distances from Earth: Moon about 400 000km, Sun about 150 000 000km, 'Around the world' races about 48 000km. King Penguin colony about 50 000.

p31 CROSSING THE RIVER
GAMES AND PUZZLES

Learning outcomes
- Understand and use the relationships between the four operations, and the principles of the arithmetic laws.
- Use brackets.
- Partition.

Lesson context
Remind the children how to solve calculations involving the use of brackets. Go on to use brackets to record ways of solving calculations using a calculator where some of the keys are 'broken'.

Setting the homework
Make sure that the children understand that they must use all the digits each time and that these digits may be used to form a larger number, e.g. if 68 was shown on a stepping stone, this could be calculated by 76 – (5 + 3), giving 76 – 8.

Back at school
Discuss the various solutions to the puzzle.

p32 ESTIMATE!
MATHS TO SHARE

Learning outcomes
- Use known number facts and place value to consolidate mental multiplication.
- Partition.
- Develop calculator skills and use a calculator effectively.

Lesson context
Encourage the children to begin multiplying mentally, a two-digit number by a single digit. Encourage estimation and discuss strategies used, focusing particularly on partitioning.

Setting the homework
Ensure that the children understand that it is necessary to estimate the numbers needed to give the desired result on the grid.

Back at school
Discuss the strategies used in order to win the game.

p33 USING GRIDS TO MULTIPLY
PRACTICE EXERCISE

Learning outcomes
- Partition.
- Approximate first. Use informal pencil and paper methods to record multiplications.
- Develop calculator skills and use a calculator effectively.

Lesson context
Remind the children that the grid method of multiplication, introduced last year, helps them to multiply larger numbers by partitioning. Estimation once again plays an important part.

Setting the homework
Encourage the children to start by estimating, before going on to draw their grids by the side of the questions and the calculations. When they have completed the work, the children may check their results using calculators. They should also make sure that the situations they choose are sensible.

Back at school
Discuss the contexts the children have chosen.
Answers: 2. 10 368, **3.** 35 934, **4.** 11 136, **5.** 158 612.

p34 CROSS-NUMBER
GAMES AND PUZZLES

Learning outcomes
- **Extend written methods to:** multiplication of ThHTU × U (short multiplication).
- Develop calculator skills and use a calculator effectively.

Lesson context
As a means of revision, children may need to use a column board to help with written multiplication of three and four digits by a single digit, before going on to short written multiplication.

Setting the homework
Remind the children to estimate before embarking on the calculations, which should be written on a separate sheet of paper. When the cross-number has been completed, it should be checked using a calculator.

Back at school
Discuss the strategies used when estimating and approximating the results. **Answers:** Across **1.** 5535, **3.** 7192, **4.** 6902, **5.** 85 Down **1.** 5076, **2.** 5022.

p35 DIVISIONS
TIMED PRACTICE EXERCISE

Learning outcome
- **Extend written methods to:** short division of TU or HTU by U (mixed number answer).

Lesson context
Informal recordings of divisions precede the formal written method, culminating in 'shorter' division with mixed numbers as results.

Setting the homework
Tell the children that both set A and set B should be timed and the times recorded on the homework sheet. Explain that you would like to see their working sheets as well as the completed homework sheet.

Back at school
Check the results and, if there is time, discuss suitable contexts for some of the questions. **Answers:** Set A **1.** $24\frac{5}{7}$, **2.** $67\frac{1}{4}$, **3.** $164\frac{3}{5}$, **4.** $150\frac{2}{3}$, **5.** $83\frac{1}{3}$, Set B **1.** $174\frac{1}{3}$, **2.** $42\frac{2}{8}$ or $\frac{1}{4}$, **3.** $62\frac{2}{7}$, **4.** $49\frac{1}{4}$, **5.** $36\frac{1}{6}$.

p36 PROBLEMS
PRACTICE EXERCISE

Learning outcome
- **Identify and use appropriate operations to solve word problems involving numbers and quantities** based on 'real life', money or measures (including time), using one or more steps.

Lesson context
It is vital that children can identify the correct operations to use when solving problems. The lesson should be spent helping with the sorting of relevant and irrelevant information together with inventing suitable contexts. This sheet gives the children an opportunity to do both.

Setting the homework
Read through the sheet with the children and make sure that they understand the questions. Encourage them to bring all their rough workings to school.

Back at school
Discuss the strategies used to solve the problems and the situations invented for question 5. **Answers: 1.** £20.65 on 15th, £18.75 on 19th, **2.** 26 or 46, **3.** 24, **4.** 104 tiles, 18 boxes.

p37 FRACTIONS EVERYWHERE
GAMES AND PUZZLES

Learning outcomes
- Recognise relationships between fractions.
- **Reduce a fraction to its simplest form by cancelling common factors** in the numerator and denominator.

Lesson context
Provide activities which involve finding the relationships between fractions, particularly equivalence and fractions written in their simplest form. Discuss how these can be found by cancelling common factors in both the numerator and the denominator.

Setting the homework
Make sure that the children understand that each statement generates a common fraction. Say that equivalent fractions will sometimes be needed, as well as fractions in their simplest form.

Back at school
Discuss the children's strategies, such as: 'I looked for fractions in the eighths family.' **Answers: 1.** $\frac{1}{8}$, **2.** $\frac{1}{5}$, **3.** $\frac{4}{5}$, **4.** $\frac{1}{4}$, **5.** $\frac{3}{4}$, **6.** $\frac{1}{2}$, **7. and 8.** $\frac{3}{4} + \frac{1}{4}$, or $\frac{4}{5} + \frac{1}{5}$, **9a.** $\frac{1}{4}$ ($\frac{2}{8}$) + $\frac{1}{8}$, **9b.** $\frac{3}{4}$ ($\frac{6}{8}$) + $\frac{1}{8}$, **10.** $\frac{1}{2}$ ($\frac{5}{10}$) + $\frac{1}{5}$ ($\frac{2}{10}$).

p38 BROADACRES PRIMARY
INVESTIGATION

Learning outcomes
- **Reduce a fraction to its simplest form by cancelling common factors** in the numerator and denominator.
- **Solve a problem by extracting and interpreting data in tables.**

Lesson context
Collect class data such as, children who wear glasses, walk to school etc. and build up a table of results including expressing results in a fractional form. Gather data from a rolling dice investigation, once more using fractions as the means of expressing what occurred, e.g. Out of 36 rolls, nine 5s were thrown, so a quarter of the throws were 5s.

Setting the homework
Explain the sheet, emphasising the need to produce as much information from the table as possible to bring back to school.

Back at school
Complete the table with the children and then ask individuals for the information they interpreted from it.
Answers: 1. 80, **2.** $\frac{1}{4}$, **3.** $\frac{1}{3}$, **4.** $\frac{1}{12}$, **5.** 108, **6.** 18, **7.** $\frac{7}{9}$, **8.** $\frac{1}{5}$, **9.** 100 girls attend the school, **10.** $\frac{1}{3}$ of the children do not have a pet.

p39 DANEHURST ROAD
PRACTICE EXERCISE

Learning outcome
- **Solve problems involving ratio and proportion ideas.**

Lesson context
Discuss and develop ratio and proportion ideas, e.g. mixing mortar (3 buckets of sand to every 1 cement), cooking recipe ratios for varying numbers of people (recipe for two re-written for six).

Setting the homework
Remind the children that ratio compares part to part and proportion compares part to whole. Explain that answers to question 1 are important as other questions use them. Make sure that they understand that in question 5 they make up new situations.

Back at school
Work through the sheet with them and try some of the questions the children bring to school. **Answers: 1.** 18, 12, 6, **2.** 28, **3.** 9, **4a.** ¼ (1 in every 4), **4b.** ¾ (3 in every 4).

p40 KAREN AND RACHAEL'S MONEY
PRACTICE EXERCISE

Learning outcomes
- **Solve simple problems involving ratio and proportion.**
- **Solve a problem by** representing, **extracting and interpreting data in tables.**

Lesson context
Discuss experiences which involve unequal sharing of, for example, sweets or marbles. Express the results first with regard to ratio and then the proportions involved. Follow this up with real life contexts, like money.

Setting the homework
Make sure the children understand that both ratios and proportions should be expressed in their simplest forms.

Back at school
Mark the questions, identifying individual problems. Discuss any interesting answers to question 6. **Answers: 1a.** ³⁄₁₀, **b.** ⁷⁄₁₀, **c.** 3 to 7, **2.** 4, 1, 2, 3, **3.** ½, **4.** ⅔, **5.** £26.

p41 OVER, UNDER AND BETWEEN
PRACTICE EXERCISE

Learning outcomes
- Use decimal notation for tenths, hundredths and thousandths.
- Order a mixed set of numbers with up to three decimal places.

Lesson context
Work with the children positioning decimal numbers on a number line, first with one and then two decimal places. Follow this by asking for numbers between, for example, 2.6 and 3.2, less than 0.7, one more than 17.3 etc.

Setting the homework
The sheet follows up the lesson with practice. Question 5 introduces a third place of decimals. It will need an introduction regarding the value of the digit.

Back at school
After marking the work, help with any problems which have arisen, e.g. digit positional value. **Answers: 1.** 6.99, 7.04, 7.18, 7.2, 7.32, 7.88, 7.9, 8, **2.** 0.7, 0.65, 0.6, 0.56, 0.47, 0.42, 0.39, 0.38, **3d.** 4.7 and 5.7, **3e.** 4.1., **5a.** 6 tenths, **5b.** 7 tens, **5c.** 2 hundredths, **5d.** 9 hundredths, **5e.** 4 thousandths, **5f.** 0 tenths or no tenths.

p42 STOP THE CLOCK FRACTIONS
TIMED PRACTICE EXERCISE

Learning outcomes
- Recognise the equivalence between the decimal and fraction forms of common fractions.
- Begin to convert a fraction to a decimal using division.
- Order fractions.
- Develop calculator skills and use a calculator effectively.

Lesson context
Change common fractions to decimal fractions using, for example, Base 10 equipment with a board, followed by calculators using division. Emphasise the need to change common fractions to decimals when ordering, e.g. ⁴⁄₉, ³⁄₇, ³⁄₃ is difficult, but 0.44, 0.43, 0.46, is much easier.

Setting the homework
Make it clear that this homework is to be timed by their helper and that calculators should only be used when necessary.

Back at school
Work through the examples but do not make too much of the solving times involved. They were only to encourage speed and to let the individual create a challenge for themselves. **Answers: Set 1a.** 0.1, **b.** 0.02, **c.** 0.5, **d.** 0.125, **e.** 0.2, **f.** 0.6666666 (using calculator), **g.** 0.375, **h.** 0.175. **Set 2a.** 0.03, **b.** 0.005, **c.** 0.25, **d.** 0.3333333 (using calculator), **e.** 0.375, **f.** 0.1111111, **g.** 0.5833333 (using calculator), **h.** 0.41. **Set 3a.** 7.75, **b.** 2.7, **c.** 8.4, **d.** 6.6666666 (using calculator), **e.** 4.125, **f.** 9.875, **g.** 0.4444444 (using calculator), **h.** 5.752.

p43 ONE TO FIFTY
INVESTIGATION

Learning outcomes
- Recognise multiples up to 10x10. Find simple common multiples.
- **Solve simple problems involving proportion.**
- **Understand percentage as the number of parts in every 100.**
- **Express simple fractions as percentages.**
- **Solve a problem by** representing **extracting and interpreting data in tables.**

Lesson context
Explore and discuss fractional answers in a survey. Go on to introduce and explain percentages (%) from the survey data. Link proportion (fraction) to percentages, e.g. 7 out of 10 people, ⁷⁄₁₀, 70%.

Setting the homework
Make the point that this homework is investigative and say that their ideas are important.

Back at school
Complete the table with them, together with the ideas introduced in question 1. Include the clarity of using percentages as against fractions. Spend some time on the children's suggestions and answers both in the table and in question 2. **Answers:** Reading across each row of the table left to right from the top: 25, 25, 12, 7; ²⁵⁄₅₀ or ½, ½, ¹²⁄₅₀ or ⁶⁄₂₅, ⁷⁄₅₀; 50%, 50%, 24%, 14%, **a.** 80%, **b.** 2%, **c.** 12%.

p44 PARIS

Learning outcomes
- **Solve a problem by** representing, **extracting and interpreting data in tables, graphs, charts.**
- Develop calculator skills and use a calculator effectively.

Lesson context
Challenge the children to plan a holiday, e.g. in Portugal from information found in a travel brochure. Decisions to include; mode and dates of travel, accommodation and car hire.

Setting the homework
Read through the information about Paris and make sure that the children understand what it conveys, including the irrelevant dates shown. Remind the children that they may use calculators.

Back at school
Give the costs of the various hotels and discuss the choices made. **Answers:** Splendide £792, Vibrant £846, Eiffel £1 248, Triomphe £1 512, Gaete £1 968.

p45 TOURING PARIS

Learning outcome
- **Solve a problem by** representing, **extracting and interpreting data in tables, graphs, charts.**

Lesson context
The children are again asked to interrogate holiday information. Many brochures provide data that will let them compare hours of sunshine.

Setting the homework
Paris and its unusual bus timetable is featured and it will be necessary to discuss this in depth to ensure that the children fully understand how 'Les Cars Blue' operate.

Back at school
Discuss the results and make time for the children to ask their questions. **Answers: 1.** 2hrs 30mins, **2.** 10, **3.** 6, **4.** 5, **5.** 13.35.

p46 FUN RUN

Learning outcome
- **Solve a problem by** representing, **extracting and interpreting data in tables, graphs, charts,** and diagrams including line graphs and bar charts with grouped discrete data.

Lesson context
Set up data, e.g. concerning Cotleigh School Swimathlon, showing the range of lengths swum, varying from 1 to 56. Discuss how to display the results in a meaningful way with a comparison of different groupings. Introduce grouping.

Setting the homework
Ask the children to read through the sheet and ensure that they understand the chart. Provide additional graph paper or photocopy it onto the back of the sheet. Remind them to label the axes of their graph and give it a title.

Back at school
Display the graphs and compare the different groupings.
Answers: 192 participants, £162 was raised.

p47 WHAT ARE THE CHANCES?

Learning outcome
- Use the language associated with probability to discuss events, including those with equally likely outcomes.

Lesson context
Using a single coin, explore and discuss the ways it may fall. Assess the chances of a head being tossed, leading to the idea of an even chance. Ask the children to predict the likely result of tossing the coin 10 times, then let them do so, recording the coin tosses and discussing their results.

Setting the homework
Make sure each child has access to a pack of cards. Tell the children to remove the appropriate cards from the pack for each question. Remind the children that when answering question 4 they should consider what, in theory, should happen (each card will appear 5 times) and compare this with the experimental results.

Back at school
Give answers and discuss question 4. **Answers: 1.** 1 in 4, **2a.** 2 in 8 or 1in 4, **b.** 1in 8, **c.** 1 in 2, **3a.** 1 in 3, **b.** 1 in 12, **c.** 1 in 4.

p48 KNOW YOUR CARS

Learning outcome
- Use the language associated with probability to discuss events.

Lesson context
Ask the child how skilful they think they are at throwing a beanbag into a wastepaper basket. Encourage ten children to try the experiment by having ten throws each and recording the results. Use these to predict how skilful a) other members of the class, b) other classes in the school might be. Invite other classes to test out predictions. Discuss how skill might improve with age etc.

Setting the homework
Read the instructions, making sure that the children understand that they must fold over the car name so that it cannot be seen. Discuss the question with the class, noting their predictions and asking for justification each time. Remind the children that the questions involve both children and adults.

Back at school
Ask individuals for their results, encouraging others to add their results and comments. Refer back to the initial predictions; how accurate were they?

SEAT

MERCEDES

PEUGEOT

CITROËN

VAUXHALL

RENAULT

PORSCHE

ROVER

HONDA

TOYOTA

p49 ESTIMATING ANGLES
TIMED PRACTICE EXERCISE

Learning outcomes
- **Use a protractor to measure angles to the nearest degree.**
- Estimate angles.

Lesson context
Question the class about angles: *what are they and how are they measured?* Ask about acute, obtuse and angles on a straight line. Using a paper-based task, ask individuals to name the angles and then estimate their measurement in degrees, giving reasons for their estimate. When complete, the children can use protractors to measure each angle. A suitable photocopiable page is provided in *100 Maths Lessons and more: Year 6*.

Setting the homework
Remind the children that this is a timed exercise and they should write their estimates on the sheet within the five minutes allowed. Only after recording all of the estimations should they go on to measure the angles.

Back at school
Give the results and ask about the strategies used to estimate the angles, e.g. a child might say: 'I knew the angle was less than a right angle but more than half way between 45° and 90° so I estimated 70° (74°)'
Answers: 1. 74°, **2.** 26°, **3.** 105°, **4.** 35°, **5.** 86°, **6.** 154°, **7.** 215°, **8.** 16°, **9.** 120°, **10.** 300°.

p50 MEASURE AND CALCULATE
PRACTICE EXERCISE

Learning outcomes
- Use a protractor to measure angles.
- Calculate angles in a triangle.
- Check that the sum of the angles of a triangle is 180°.

Lesson context
A large triangle drawn on a thin sheet of card is needed to demonstrate and find the sum of the angles. Cut out and put the three angles of the triangle at a point on a line showing that their sum is 180°. To show that this is not a special triangle, set the children the same task of drawing any triangle and cutting off the vertices.

Setting the homework
Once again, remind the class that the sum of the angles of a triangle is 180° and ask how they intend to calculate the third angle of each triangle.

Back at school
Mark the activity together and discuss the accuracy involved.
Answers: Here are the correct answers but allow some latitude. **a.** 42° 63°, **b.** 25° 112°, **c.** 34° 96°, **d.** 27° 36°, **e.** 17° 100°, **f.** 38° 44°, the third angles are: **a.** 75°, **b.** 43°, **c.** 50°, **d.** 117°, **e.** 63°, **f.** 98°.

p51 MAKING TRIANGLES
INVESTIGATION

Learning outcome
- Classify triangles (Year 5 revision).

Lesson context
Provide a 3 × 3 matrix arrangement and six attribute cards as shown: The children are encouraged to make triangles to fit the nine boxes on the grid. The lesson concludes with a discussion about the empty boxes.

	Having all acute angles	Having a right angle	Having an obtuse angle
All sides the same length	1	2	3
Two sides the same length	4	5	6
All sides different lengths	7	8	9

Setting the homework
Read the sheet with the class and remind them of the attributes of specific triangles. Discuss how the children might tackle the problem.

Back at school
Compare results and findings.
Answers: Certain combinations of straws will not make a triangle 4, 4, 8; 4, 4, 5; and 4, 6, 10.

p52 I'M THINKING OF...
MATHS TO SHARE

Learning outcomes
- Classify triangles (Year 5 revision) and quadrilaterals using criteria such as parallel sides, equal angles, equal sides.
- Make and investigate a general statement about familiar shapes by finding examples which satisfy it.

Lesson context
Sorting quadrilaterals using the Venn diagram shown below, leading to general statements like, 'Quadrilaterals with one pair of parallel sides are trapeziums'.

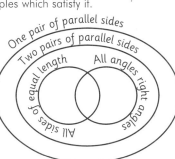

Setting the homework
Read the rules of the game with the children. Discuss some of the attributes they might choose such as, 'My shape has all its angles the same', then, 'It does not have any parallel sides' (regular pentagon).

Back at school
Discuss the game and any interesting results.

p53 CUBES AGAIN
GAMES AND PUZZLES

Learning outcomes
- Make shapes with increasing accuracy.
- Visualise 3-D shapes from 2-D drawings.

Lesson context
Ask the children to tell you all they can about a cube, 'It's got 12 edges', 'All the faces are squares' etc. Encourage the children to investigate nets of a cube, sketching all those possible. Select one and construct it accurately.

Setting the homework
Encourage the children to consider the strategies they used to sketch the closed cube. For the homework, it might help if they use rough or squared paper and cut out possible nets before sketching them. Remind them that they should have sharp pencils and suitable instruments to construct their chosen open cube accurately.

Back at school
Display homework sheets and accurately drawn open cubes.

p54 PERIMETERS AND FORMULAE

Learning outcomes
- **Calculate the perimeter of simple shapes.**
- Make and investigate a general statement about familiar shapes by finding examples which satisfy it. Develop from explaining a generalised relationship in words to expressing it in a formula using symbols.

Lesson context
Discuss how to express the relationships between lengths of sides and perimeters of regular polygons. Move from words, to expressing it in a formula using symbols. For example, considering a regular octagon; 'The perimeter p is found by multiplying the value of one side, l, by 8'; $p = l \times 8$ $(p = 8l)$.

Setting the homework
This activity reinforces the relationship between the length of a side and the perimeter of a regular polygon, using words and the corresponding formula.

Back at school
Work through the activity together and discuss the strategies used. Note any common problems experienced and clarify misconceptions. **Answers: 1.** Measure the length of one side and multiply the value by 4; $p = l \times 4$, $(p = 4l)$ where l is the value of one side and p the perimeter. **2.** Regular heptagons because the perimeter lengths are always seven times the value of one side. **3.** $P = l \times 12$, $(p = 12l)$; 72cm.
4. $P = (a \times 10) + (b \times 4)$, $(p = 10a + 4b)$; 11cm.

p55 MEASUREMENTS EVERYWHERE

Learning outcome
- Use read and write standard metric units (km, cm, kg, g, l, ml, cl) including their abbreviations and relationships between them.

Lesson context
Arrange the class into groups. One group practises metric equivalencies and applies these units to the 'real world', while other groups work on length, mass and capacity. Let these children estimate and measure, using objects and containers. They should consider suitable units, degrees of accuracy and equipment.

Setting the homework
Make the point that this is a shared homework. Encourage a clear report, stating how the investigation was carried out, together with lists of measurements showing the units found.

Back at school
Read the reports. Make comprehensive class lists under Length, Mass (Weight), Capacity and Area and create a display.

p56 FIND THE PARTNER

Learning outcomes
- Consolidate all strategies from previous year.
- Partition.
- Choose and use appropriate ways of calculating: mental, mental with jottings.
- Check with an equivalent calculation.

Lesson context
Discuss various strategies of mental calculation using larger numbers and decimals. Include doubling, adding on to find differences, rounding numbers and adjusting. Encourage a variety of strategies and checking methods, using equivalent calculations.

Setting the homework
All calculations must be done mentally but jottings can be used when applicable. Stress that all strategies must be recorded on a separate sheet and brought to school.

Back at school
Mark the work with the children and highlight the variety of strategies they used. **Answers: 1.** with e, **2.** with d, **3.** with a, **4.** with h, **5.** with f, **6.** with c, **7.** with b, **8.** with g. **9.** i) 5, ii) 2.

p57 WALK THE TIGHTROPE

Learning outcomes
- Use known number facts and place value to consolidate mental addition and subtraction.
- Check using a calculator.

Lesson context
Ask the children to suggest strategies to tackle mental addition, including decimals. Discuss their ideas and use suitable games, in pairs, with the level of difficulty based on the ability of the children.

Setting the homework
Run through the rules with the children.

Back at school
Talk to the children about the games they played.

p58 DECICALC ADDITIONS

Learning outcome
- **Extend written methods to column addition of numbers involving decimals.**

Lesson context
Consolidate vertical addition of whole numbers and then extend to decimals. Present the additions horizontally ($26.42 + 117.08$) and emphasise the care that is needed with the vertical layout. Precede calculation with estimation. Encourage 'real life' contexts. Let the children check their answers using a calculator.

$$26.42$$
$$117.08$$

Setting the homework
The homework allows practice of the lesson content. Mention that calculators are not to be used and that the estimation strategies are an important aspect of the work.

Back at school
Mark the work with the children, using calculators for answers. Invite individuals to describe the estimation strategies they used by referring to their notes. **Answers: 1.** 196.12, **2.** 8.29, **3.** 1256.1, **4.** 44.3, **5.** 88.77.

p59 DECICALC SUBTRACTIONS
PRACTICE EXERCISE

Learning outcomes
- **Extend written methods to column subtraction of numbers involving decimals.**
- **Solve word problems involving numbers and quantities** based on 'real life', money or measures.
- Round a number with two decimal places to the nearest tenth or to the nearest whole number.
- Check with the inverse operation when using a calculator.

Lesson context
Move from vertical subtraction of whole numbers to decimal calculations. Present the subtractions horizontally and make sure that the children use the correct vertical layout by lining up the decimal points. Estimation, rounding and 'real life' applications should also feature. Answers can be checked using a calculator.

16.30

7.65

Setting the homework
Explain that the homework gives practice of the lesson content.

Back at school
Use calculators for checking answers. Ask children for their estimation strategies and their realistic suggestions for addition and subtraction of decimals, using different measures. **Answers: 1.** 11.72, **2.** 26.03, **3.** 3.61, **4.** 233.37, **5.** 257.6, **6.** £3.57, **7.** 1 701.6 miles (1 701 or 1 700 miles rounded).

p60 SQUARE NUMBER CHALLENGE
GAMES AND PUZZLES

Learning outcomes
- Recognise squares of numbers to 12x12.
- Use known number facts and place value to consolidate mental addition/ subtraction/ multiplication/ division.

Lesson context
Work with the children to develop the sequence of square numbers from squares:

etc.,

and by using multiplication. Introduce the notation of 1^2, 2^2, 3^2 etc. Let them work in pairs with, for example, equilateral triangles:

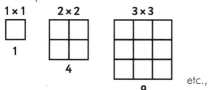

etc.,

and parallelograms:

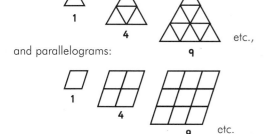

etc.

Let the children use multiplication to extend the sequence to 12 x 12 and beyond.

Setting the homework
Explain the sheet and work through the answers given for question 1. Ask for other possibilities e.g. $6^2 \div 2^2$.

Back at school
Ask an individual child for their set of answers to a question. Invite other possibilities until no other suggestions are forthcoming. **Answers:** Various.

p61 SEQUENCES AND TERM NUMBERS
INVESTIGATION

Learning outcomes
- Recognise and extend number sequences such as the sequence of square numbers.
- Recognise square numbers to at least 12x12.
- Use known number facts and place value to consolidate mental addition/ subtraction/ multiplication and division.
- Make and investigate general statements about familiar numbers.
- Develop calculator skills and use a calculator effectively.

Lesson context
Explore the difference pattern generated from the square number sequence:

Introduce the word 'term' e.g. 36 is the 6th term (6 x 6). Find the value of other terms e.g. 14th term, 196 (14 x 14). Go on to build up successive terms, colouring squares on graph paper: Record the building 1, 1 + 3, 1 + 3 + 5 etc. Discuss square numbers being generated from the sum of consecutive odd numbers e.g. the 5th square number is the sum of the first five odd numbers, 1 + 3 + 5 + 7 + 9.

Setting the homework
The homework develops the lesson content. This is quite a long, and for some children, a challenging investigation. For less able children, select those parts of it which you feel they can tackle and give them any necessary help.

Back at school
Mark the work together and ask individuals how they approached 4b and c. Discuss the other sequences and term numbers investigated by the children. **Answers: 1.** 5th 25; 6th 36; 7th 49. **a.** 12, **b.** 169, **c.** 1 600, **d.** 10 000, **2.** 4th 25; 5th 34; 6th 45; 7th 58. **3a.** -4, -1, 4, 11, 20, **b.** 4, 16, 36, 64, 100, **c.** 0.5, 2, 4.5, 8, 12.5, **4b.** n2 + 13, **c.** n2 ÷ 4.

p62 PASCAL'S TRIANGLE
INVESTIGATION

Learning outcomes
- Recognise and extend number sequences such as the sequence of triangular numbers.
- Make and investigate general statements about familiar numbers.

Lesson context
The children use pegs and pegboards or spotted paper to build triangles and develop the triangular number sequence:

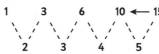

1 cannot be made from a triangle and can only be justified by the difference pattern built 'backwards'.

Explore triangular numbers as the sum of consecutive counting numbers i.e 1, 1 + 2, 1 + 2 + 3 etc and link to square numbers being the sum of consecutive odd numbers.

Setting the homework
Discuss the activity and point out the clues to aid the investigation. Make sure that they appreciate that they must write a report.

Back at school
Develop children's suggestions from their reports.
Answers: The next three rows are: 1 6 15 20 15 6 1; 1 7 21 35 35 21 7 1; 1 8 28 56 70 56 28 8 1. Considering the array from either direction, the diagonals are: ones; counting numbers; triangular numbers (sum of the first 'n' counting numbers); tetrahedral numbers (sum of the first 'n' triangular numbers). The numbers in each succeeding diagonal(s) are generated from the previous diagonal. A line of symmetry runs vertically down the array. Row totals are doubling.

TERM 2

p63 ABOUT HOW MANY?

INVESTIGATION

Learning outcomes
- Use the vocabulary of estimation and approximation.
- Consolidate rounding an integer to the nearest 100 000, 10 000 or 1 000.
- **Use appropriate operations to solve word problems involving numbers and quantities** based on 'real life'.
- Develop calculator skills and use a calculator effectively.

Lesson context
Provide activities involving ordering numbers to a million and rounding to the nearest 1 000 or 10 000. Estimating the sums and differences between pairs of large numbers by employing rounding. Explore the question, 'What is a billion?'.

Setting the homework
Explain the sheet, emphasising the importance of clear layouts.

Back at school
Discuss each question and the strategies for estimation and approximation used by the children. Spend time on any interesting ideas developed for question 4.
Answers: 1. various, **2a.** about 730 000, **b.** about 17 500 000, **c.** 67 generations allowing 30 years for a generation, **3a.** about 100 000, **b.** about 37 000 000.

p64 GOALS!

MATHS TO SHARE

Learning outcomes
- Find the difference between a positive and a negative integer, or two negative integers.
- **Solve a problem** by representing **and interpreting data in tables.**

Lesson context
Work with the children to order a set of jumbled integers on the board. Let the children walk a number line marked from –10 to 10 to answer questions such as, 6–8?, –1–9? Record results and describe the statements in temperature terms, e.g. 'the temperature fell 8°C from 6°C to –2°C'. Introduce the 'sign change' key on the calculator in order to calculate, for example, –6–3.

Setting the homework
Discuss how negative numbers are used in deciding league positions if teams have the same number of points. Explain the sheet and mention that the newspaper league tables may split the goals 'for' (F) and 'against' (A) into home and away. For example:

HOME		AWAY	
F	A	F	A
15	30	24	37

gives a total of goals F 39 A 67 and a goal difference of –28.

Back at school
Mark and discuss the questions, asking individuals for their answers to question 3. **Answers: 1.** Torquay United's goal difference was better than Lincoln City's by 4, **2.** 19th Tranmere Rovers, difference 1, 20th Halifax Town, difference –11, 21st Exeter City –12, 22nd Cambridge United –15.

p65 FIND THE CLUES

GAMES AND PUZZLES

Learning outcomes
- **Extend written methods to** ThHTU x U (short multiplication).
- Estimate by approximating.

Lesson context
Work with the children to solve the multiplication of a 3-digit number by a single digit, setting out the calculation as a short multiplication. Asking for estimates first. Extend the work to larger numbers multiplied by a single digit, checking with the calculator.

Setting the homework
Discuss the sheet and remind the children to bring all their rough working to the lesson.

Back at school
Check their results and discuss the strategies used.
Answers: Clues across; **1.** 342 x 4, **3.** 786 x 9, **4.** 545 x 3, **5.** 3 683 x 8. Clues down; **2.** 175 x 5, **3.** 851 x 9, **4.** 26 x 7.

p66 FIRST TO THE TOP

MATHS TO SHARE

Learning outcomes
- Use known number facts and place value to consolidate mental multiplication and division.
- Estimate by approximating.
- Develop calculator skills and use a calculator effectively.

Lesson context
Children begin by multiplying multiples of 10 by a single digit mentally and explaining their strategies. Move from large numbers to decimals, e.g. 0.4 x 3 and finally 0.04 x 3.

Setting the homework
Read through the rules of the game, reminding the children that each answer should be checked with the calculator. Give the children a half sheet of A4 card to make their function cards in advance.

Back at school
Discuss the strategies that were used.

p67 DECORATING

PRACTICE EXERCISE

Learning outcomes
- Approximate first. Use informal pencil and paper methods to support, record or explain multiplications.
- Develop calculator skills and use a calculator effectively.

Lesson context
Children use their own pencil and paper methods to multiply a number with two decimal places by a single digit and discuss their strategies.

Setting the homework
Read through the sheet and remind the children that they are to use their own pencil and paper methods but they must record these methods on the rough paper and be prepared to discuss them.

Back at school
Give the answers and discuss the strategies used.
Answers: paint £20.25, wallpaper £18.20, carpet £83.07, curtains £35.16, Total £156.68 with £43.32 not spent. Posters £14.97. Amount left £28.35.

p68 MULTIPLICATIONS PRACTICE EXERCISE

Learning outcomes
- **Extend written methods to:** short multiplication of numbers involving decimals.
- Estimate by approximating then check result.
- Develop calculator skills and use a calculator effectively.

Lesson context
The children work together to solve multiplication of decimals using a column board, leading to practice of the written form, short multiplication.

Setting the homework
Stress that the homework is to be timed by their helper and calculators should not be used. The children should work on the sheet, using the paper to write their 'real life' contexts.

Back at school
Give the answers and discuss the children's 'real life' contexts.
Answers: Set 1 – 1. 14.48, **2.** 25.02, **3.** 19.74, **4.** 56.63, **5.** 49.14, **Set 2 – 1.** 36.15, **2.** 74.72, **3.** 15, **4.** 28.92, **5.** 20.91.

p69 FIND THE FUNCTION GAMES AND PUZZLES

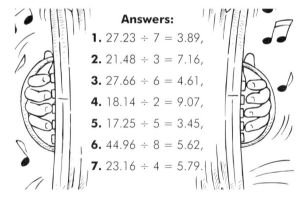

Learning outcome
- Approximate first. Use informal pencil and paper methods to support, record or explain multiplications and divisions.

Lesson context
Children use their own pencil and paper methods of multiplication to solve division calculations as a pre-cursor to short division.

Setting the homework
Make sure that the children know what is expected from them and emphasise that all working should be done on rough paper which should accompany the homework sheet.

Back at school
Give the answers and discuss ways of working.

Answers:
1. 27.23 ÷ 7 = 3.89,
2. 21.48 ÷ 3 = 7.16,
3. 27.66 ÷ 6 = 4.61,
4. 18.14 ÷ 2 = 9.07,
5. 17.25 ÷ 5 = 3.45,
6. 44.96 ÷ 8 = 5.62,
7. 23.16 ÷ 4 = 5.79.

p70 DECIMAL DIVISIONS TIMED PRACTICE EXERCISES

Learning outcome
- **Extend written methods to: short division of numbers involving decimals.**

Lesson context
Moving on from the children's own methods of division, short division of decimals is introduced and time is given for practice.

Setting the homework
The homework develops from the lesson content. Make sure that the children have paper to work on and that they know that this must be returned with the homework.

Back at school
Give the answers and look at the written sheets. Discuss the 'real life' contexts and their suitability.
Answers: Set 1 – 1. 17.4, **2.** 16.3, **3.** 36.9, **4.** 14.7, **5.** 24.8, **Set 2 – 1.** 54.7, **2.** 74.4, **3.** 97.2, **4.** 27.3, **5.** 28.9.

p71 CASH AND CARRY PRACTICE EXERCISE

Learning outcome
- Develop calculator skills and use a calculator effectively.

Lesson context
The children investigate the 'Memory' facility of the calculator, namely [M+], [M–], [MR] and [MC] or [AC]. Solve bracket calculations such as (43 x 8) + (27 x 9) and go on to discuss the use of Memory in 'real life' calculations.

Setting the homework
Tell the children to use the calculator to do the calculations, but only write the answers.

Back at school
Discuss how the 'Memory' was used.
Answers: £23.58.

p72 TINSCOMBE TOWN SURVEY PRACTICE EXERCISE

Learning outcomes
- Use the vocabulary of approximation.
- Recognise when two fractions are equivalent. (Year 5)
- **Use a fraction as an 'operator' to find fractions of numbers.**
- **Reduce a fraction to its simplest form by cancelling common factors.**

Lesson context
Revise work on equivalent fractions and simplest form, linking these ideas to surveys, e.g. favourite sport – 150 questioned ⅔rds said soccer, ⅕th swimming, by using the fractions as operators. [100, 30]

Setting the homework
The survey and exercises give practice of the lesson content. Mention that fractional answers should be in their simplest form and that calculators should not be used.

Back at school
Work through the sheet with them. **Answers: 1.** 36 000, **2a.** 1 680, **b.** 1 600, **c.** 1 400, **d.** 600, **e.** 2 000, **3a.** ⅓, **b.** ³⁄₁₀.

p73 ROUND UP OR DOWN? PRACTICE EXERCISE

Learning outcomes
- Round a number with one, two or more decimal places to the nearest tenth or whole.
- Round up or down after division.
- Develop calculator skills and use a calculator effectively.

Lesson context
Write a set of decimal numbers and discuss rounding them up to the nearest tenth and then to the nearest whole number. Emphasise that 7.45 is 7.5 to the nearest tenth and that 10.5 is 11 to the nearest whole number. Try to measure a child's height in millimetres but express it to the nearest centimetre. Talk about, for example, 3.72 litres of water rounded to the nearest litre. Use calculators for divisions, once again rounding answers to the nearest tenth or whole number.

Setting the homework
The exercises provide practice of the lesson content.

Back at school
Mark the work, helping individuals with any problems.
Answers: 1a. 6, 6.4, **b.** 18, 17.9, **c.** 100, 99.8, **d.** 28, 28.1, **e.** 0, 0.4, **2a.** 3, **b.** 2, **c.** 2, **d.** 34, **e.** 123, **3a.** 8.3, **b.** 4.3, **c.** 0.1, **d.** 3.8, **e.** 2 248.2, **4.** highest 80.4kg, lowest 79.5kg.

p74 LOW TO HIGH AND ROUND ABOUT

PRACTICE EXERCISE

Learning outcomes

- Order fractions by converting them to fractions with a common denominator.
- Convert a fraction to a decimal using division.
- Develop calculator skills and use a calculator effectively.

Lesson context

Work with the children ordering common fractions by first converting them to fractions with a common denominator and later to decimals using divisions and a calculator.

Setting the homework

Remind the children that rough paper and their record is needed. Calculators are required for questions 3 and 4 only.

Back at school

Work through the sheet asking individuals how they tackled the questions. **Answers: 1a.** $\frac{1}{8}$, $\frac{1}{4}$, **b.** 0, 1/8, **c.** $\frac{3}{8}$, $\frac{1}{2}$, **d.** $\frac{1}{2}$, $\frac{3}{4}$, **e.** $\frac{1}{2}$, $\frac{3}{4}$, **2a.** $\frac{12}{30}$, $\frac{25}{30}$, $\frac{15}{30}$, $\frac{5}{30}$, $\frac{10}{30}$; $\frac{1}{6}$, $\frac{1}{3}$, $\frac{1}{2}$, $\frac{2}{3}$, $\frac{5}{6}$, **b.** $\frac{12}{20}$, $\frac{10}{20}$, $\frac{7}{20}$, $\frac{5}{20}$, $\frac{8}{20}$; $\frac{1}{4}$, $\frac{7}{20}$, $\frac{2}{5}$, $\frac{1}{2}$, $\frac{3}{5}$, **3a.** 0.375, 0.266, 0.66, 0.33, 0.58, 0.66; $\frac{4}{15}$, $\frac{1}{3}$, $\frac{3}{8}$, $\frac{7}{12}$, $\frac{3}{5}$, $\frac{2}{3}$, **b.** 0.83, 0.875, 0.857, 0.8, 0.9, 0.81; $\frac{4}{5}$, $\frac{13}{16}$, $\frac{5}{6}$, $\frac{6}{7}$, $\frac{7}{8}$, $\frac{9}{10}$, **4.** $\frac{1}{4}$ (all the decimal answers, rounded to 2 decimal places lie between 0.2 and 0.3 namely 0.23, 0.27, 0.2, 0.3, 0.22, 0.29).

p75 CONNECTIONS

PRACTICE EXERCISE

Learning outcomes

- Convert a fraction to a decimal.
- Express simple fractions as percentages.
- **Find simple percentages of small whole number quantities.**
- **Solve a problem** by representing **extracting and interpreting data in tables.**

Lesson context

Explore some relationships between common and decimal fractions including recurring decimals e.g. $\frac{1}{3}$, $\frac{2}{3}$, $\frac{1}{9}$. Go on to consider percentage equivalents to simple fractions.

Setting the homework

The exercises provide practice of the lesson content.

Back at school

Use the strategies the children employed to emphasise the relationships between common fractions, decimals and percentages and their extensive use in the 'real world'. **Answers:** The table: $\frac{1}{5}$, 0.2, 20%; $\frac{3}{10}$, 0.3, 30%, $\frac{7}{10}$, 0.7, 70%; $\frac{1}{1}$, 1.0, 100%; $\frac{1}{2}$, 0.5, 50%; $\frac{1}{4}$, 0.25, 25%; $\frac{1}{8}$, 0.125, 12.5%; $\frac{1}{3}$, 0.33 recurring, 33$\frac{1}{3}$%; $\frac{2}{3}$, 0.66, 66$\frac{2}{3}$%. **a.** 0.4, **b.** 0.75, 75%, **c.** 2.666, **d.** 0.85%, **e.** £200, **f.** £150.

p76 POLYHEDRA

INVESTIGATION

Learning outcomes

- Explain methods and reasoning orally and in writing.
- Develop from explaining a generalised relationship in words to expressing it in a formula using letters as symbols.
- Visualise 3-D shapes from 2-D drawings.

Lesson context

Investigating the relationship between the diameter and circumference of a circle using apparatus such as plates and jars leading to a generalised relationship and the symbol _.

Setting the homework

Read through the sheet and name the 3-D shapes. These drawings help with the investigation and their reports should include a relationship between faces, vertices and edges.

Back at school

Ask individuals to read their reports and extend the relationships they offer to a formula in words and then symbols. **Answers:** The sum of the number of faces and vertices is always two more than the number of edges.
E.g: $F + V = E + 2$ or $F + V - 2 = E$.

p77 PENTAGONS FROM CIRCLES

PRACTICE EXERCISE

Learning outcomes

- Make shapes with increasing accuracy.
- Calculate angles in a triangle or around a point.
- **Use a protractor to measure** and draw **acute and obtuse angles to the nearest degree.**

Lesson context

Show the children how to construct regular polygons from circles, by splitting the angle at the centre into the number of sides of the shape under construction. For example, to construct a hexagon, the angle at the centre of the circle should be split into six equal angles of 60° and six radii drawn.

Setting the homework

Remind the children that the polygons that have been constructed were regular. The homework gives the opportunity to use the same method to construct irregular polygons.

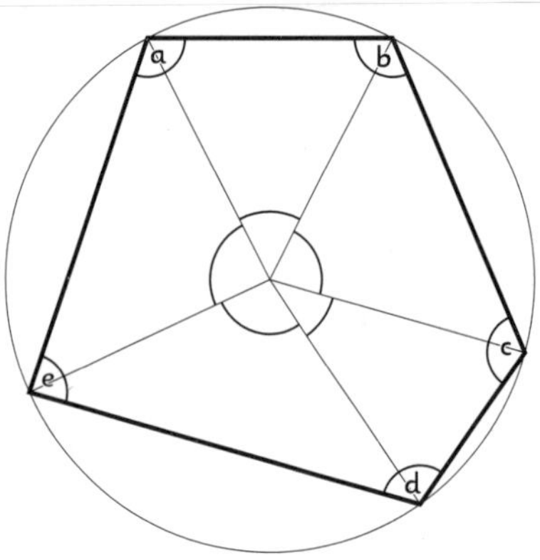

Back at school

Check the answers and look at the children's hexagon constructions. **Answers: a.** 109°, **b.** 113.5°, **c.** 121°, **d.** 110°, **e.** 86.5°.

p78 STRAWS AND PIPE-CLEANERS

MATHS TO SHARE

Learning outcomes

- Describe and visualise properties of solid shapes.
- Make and investigate a general statement about familiar shapes by finding examples which satisfy it.

Lesson context

Talk about the attributes of 3-D shapes and play a game. Given a set of solid shapes, one child thinks of an attribute which some of the set have. By 'Yes/No' questioning, the other children have to determine this attribute.

Setting the homework

Collect some pipe-cleaners and cut them into lengths of about 2cm. Give a few to each child. Read through the sheet, making sure that the children understand how the straws and pipe-cleaners form the skeletal polyhedra. Emphasise that only polyhedra (having all straight sides) may be constructed and it might be necessary to cut some of the straws.

Back at school

Ask individuals to give their results, including the numbers of straws for which a polyhedra was impossible. **Answers:** The least number of straws needed was 6. Any number of straws above 6 and divisible by 3 will make a prism, e.g. 15 straws will make a pentagonal prism, 5 for each of the base and top and 5 for the sides. Any number of straws, 6 and above and divisible by 2 will make a pyramid, e.g. 16 straws will make an octagonal pyramid, 8 straws for the base and 8 for the sides.

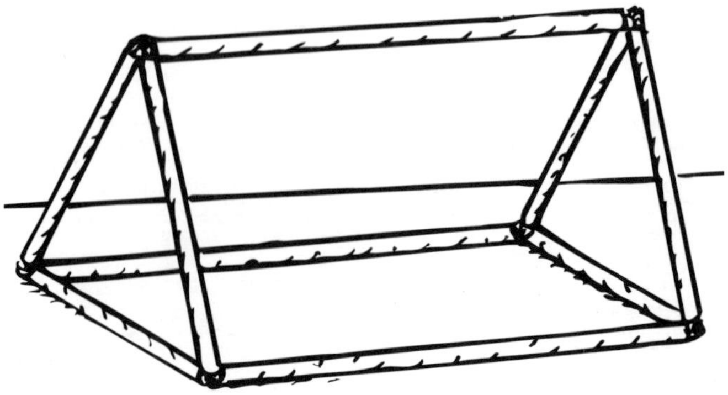

SHAPES USING CO-ORDINATES

p79 — PRACTICE EXERCISE

Learning outcome
• **Read and plot co-ordinates in all four quadrants.**

Lesson context
Move from a single quadrant graph to a four quadrant graph, giving the children opportunity to both plot and read co-ordinates.

Setting the homework
Give out the graph paper and draw attention to the illustration at the top, labelling the quadrants and then reading through the sheet.

Back at school
Discuss the homework and any observations noted, e.g. 'two of the 'x' values and two of the 'y' values are the same'.

CO-ORDINATES – REFLECTIONS

p80 — PRACTICE EXERCISE

Learning outcomes
• **Read and plot co-ordinates in all four quadrants.**
• Recognise where a shape will be after reflection in two mirror lines at right angles.

Lesson context
Begin by reflecting shapes in one mirror line. Go on to reflecting shapes in two mirror lines at right angles and discussing strategies.

Setting the homework
Remind the children of the strategies they used in the lesson.

Back at school
Display and discuss the results. **Answers:** Triangle reflected through the 'x' axis (6,–6) (9,–10) (11,–4); reflected through the 'y' axis (–6,6) (–9,10) (–11,4); Rectangle reflected through the 'x'axis (3,–1) (1,–3) (5,–7) (7,–5); reflected through the 'y' axis (–3,1) (–1,3) (–5,7) (–7,5).

WHERE'S THE SHAPE?

p81 — PRACTICE EXERCISE

Learning outcomes
• Recognise where a shape will be after reflection in a mirror line touching the shape at a point; in two mirror lines at right angles.
• **Use a protractor to measure** and draw **acute and obtuse angles to the nearest degree.**

Lesson context
Discuss the position of an image when a triangle, is;
a) touching the mirror line at a point
b) reflected in two mirror lines at right angles.
The children can sketch images from given shapes.

Setting the homework
Tell the children that this homework is going to involve them in constructing shapes accurately, so their pencils must be sharp, protractors and rulers clear. Children experiencing difficulty with construction may sketch the results. Emphasise that the image of the pentagon is shown by the dotted line and the original shape should be constructed.

Back at school
Ask individuals to show and explain their results.

AREAS EVERYWHERE

p82 — MATHS TO SHARE

Learning outcomes
• **Calculate the area of simple compound shapes that can be split into rectangles.**
• Explain a generalised relationship in words and express it in a formula.
• Record readings from scales to a suitable degree of accuracy.
• Develop calculator skills and use a calculator effectively.

Lesson context
Develop statements for finding the area of any rectangle, first in words and then using letters. Provide examples involving m, cm and mm. Estimate and find areas in school.

Setting the homework
Discuss question 2 and say that questions 3 and 4 need a helper.

Back at school
Mark the work together, making sure that reasonable measurements are suggested for question 3. Discuss areas in question 4 which were not just one rectangle.
Answers: 1. ...of the length and b the value of the breadth, **2.** 90cm, **3.** various, with heights around 2.4m.

PUZZLING SHAPES

p83 — GAMES AND PUZZLES

Learning outcome
• **Calculate the area of simple shapes** by relating them to rectangles.

Lesson context
Involve the children in activities which allow them to calculate the area of simple compound shapes that can be split into rectangles. Encourage them to say how they are splitting the shapes and what measurements they intend to use.

Setting the homework
Explain that they are now going on to calculate areas of parallelograms and a triangle by developing the ideas established in the lesson. Give some help to the less able.

Back at school
Ask individuals to describe how they tackled the puzzles.
Answers: 1a. 18cm^2, **1b.** 18cm^2, **2.** 10cm^2, **3.** 128cm^2, **4.** 150cm^2.

WHICH WAY?

p84 — INVESTIGATION

Learning outcomes
• Know rough equivalents of miles and kilometres.
• **Solve a problem by** representing **and interpreting data in diagrams.**
• Develop calculator skills and use a calculator effectively.

Lesson context
Discuss a road distance chart in kilometres before using it to find the distances between towns and /or cities. Build up a conversion table, kilometres to miles i.e.1 km is about 0.62 miles. Use calculators for mileages between places. Construct a distance scale marked in both kilometres and miles.

Setting the homework
Read through the sheet, encouraging them to find as many different Exeter to Totnes routes as they can.

Back at school
Mark the work. Find out who found the greatest number of Exeter to Totnes routes. Discuss other routes drawn in this way e.g. London Underground Map. **Answers:** The map is not to scale. Mileages: Exeter to Dawlish 13, to Teignmouth 14, to Newton Abbot 16, to Totnes 28. Dawlish to Teignmouth 3. Teignmouth to Newton Abbot 6, to Torquay 9. Torquay to Paignton 3, to Totnes 9, to Newton Abbot 7. Paignton to Totnes 6. Totnes to Newton Abbot 9.

p85 PINBALL

Learning outcomes
- Find the mode and range of a set of data.
- Develop calculator skills and use a calculator effectively.

Lesson context
Collect data relating to shoe sizes of the class and, after a discussion about the meaning of the words 'range' and 'mode', the children can use the data to find both. Ask them for other sets of data where range and mode might be considered e.g. a batsman's cricket scores (0, 0, 32, 0, 17, 0, 10, 14). What kind of player might he be?

Setting the homework
Read the sheet together and tell the children that they will not need calculators except perhaps in their own questions.

Back at school
Ask individuals for their results to the first part of the exercise before going on to hear individual questions. Discuss whether finding the mode was useful. **Answers: a.** Jan: 5 to 105, Kumar: 0 to 110, **b.** Jan 35, Kumar 60.

p86 COMPUTER VOUCHERS

Learning outcomes
- Find the mode and range of a set of data. Begin to find the mean of a set of data.
- Develop calculator skills and use a calculator effectively.

Lesson context
Continue the theme of 'average'. The lesson could begin with a discussion centred around the statement, 'Buy the new VW Golf for excellent fuel consumption! It will average 42 miles to the gallon'. Discuss other contexts like, 'average rainfall' and 'the number of cars travelling along a road per hour', before introducing the concept of mean.

Setting the homework
Discuss the school notice; what can the children tell you about it? If necessary, remind the class of the meaning of the various forms of average.

Back at school
Give the answers. Discuss the calculator result for the mean. Ask individuals for their questions. **Answers:** Range 63–158, mode 82, median 87, mean 98.

p87 PULSE RATES

Learning outcomes
- Find the mode and range of a set of data. Begin to find the median and mean of a set of data.
- Develop calculator skills and use a calculator effectively.

Lesson context
This final lesson introduces median and gives the children practice in finding the three different forms of average in context, e.g. numbers of brothers and sisters, swimming times over one length.

Setting the homework
Tell the children that they are going to use data about themselves (their pulse rates) for homework. Show the children how to take their own pulse and give them a minute or two to practise. Time the class over one minute and record the results, names are not necessary. Ensure that each child has a copy of the results to take home.

Back at school
Allow time for the children to report their findings.

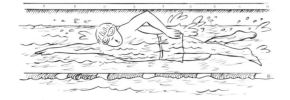

p88 GUESS THE GRAPH

Learning outcome
- **Solve a problem by extracting and interpreting data in tables and graphs.**

Lesson context
Let the children interpret and draw distance/time graphs involving, for example, car and rail travel. Include finding and discussing average (mean) speeds.

Setting the homework
It is not necessary to precede this homework with any discussion as it is intended for individual interpretation at home.

Back at school
Discuss the graph and ask for individual comments.
Answers: A possible context for the data could be a person walking, stopping for coffee and lunch, before returning home on the bus.

p89 REPEAT IT

Learning outcomes
- Recognise and extend number sequences.
- Use the relationship between addition and subtraction and multiplication and division.

Lesson context
Explore addition, subtraction, multiplication and division sequences with the children. Introduce negative integers and decimals in the sequences, bearing in mind varying abilities. Discuss their strategies, in particular, repeating functions and relationships between the four operations.

Setting the homework
The homework is presented as a series of sequence puzzles and follows up the lesson content. Remind the children of the important strategies which have emerged. Consider which questions the less able can tackle.

Back at school
Talk through the strategies used and try some of the questions brought in by the children. **Answers: 1.** +4; 6, 14, 22, **2.** +12; 2, 26, 50, **3.** –5 (subtract 5); 0, –5, –15, **4.** +11; 0.4, 22.4, 44.4, **5.** –0.6 (subtract 0.6); 17.4, 16.2, **6.** –0.9 (subtract 0.9); 4.5, 2.7, 4 times, **7.** x5; 5, 125, **8.** 405, 45, 5, **9.** x7; 3.5, 171.5, 1 200.5, **10a.** +16, **b.** 31, 47, 63, 79.

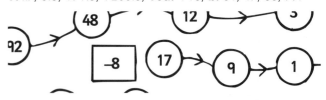

p90 FUNCTION FUN

Learning outcome
- Recognise and explain patterns and relationships, generalise and predict.

Lesson context
Let the children choose a number (input). You apply a function, e.g. +12 to it and record the output. Continue in this way using the same function each time. Let them guess the function you are using. Move to two functions, e.g. x3 followed by +2. Split the class into ability groups exploring other functions in this game form. Encourage the more able children to use combinations of all four operations, together with squaring, e.g. square and add one. Discuss problem calculations, e.g. input 1, –4, x6 or input 17, ÷3, x7.

Setting the homework
Make sure that the children understand the Function fun rules.

Back at school
The children report any interesting aspects of the games they played. **Answers: 2.** x7, +3.

(p91) TARGET PRACTICE — PRACTICE EXERCISE

Learning outcomes
- Consolidate all strategies from previous year, including: find a difference by counting up; use the relationship between addition and subtraction; add several numbers.
- Use known number facts and place value to consolidate mental addition/subtraction.
- Use appropriate ways of calculating; mental, mental with jottings.

Lesson context
Concentrate on mental addition and subtraction calculations. Discuss strategies for the examples. Go on to include some which involve jottings. Provide some practice examples.

Setting the homework
The homework provides further practice of the lesson content.

Back at school
Give the answers and discuss the strategies used by the children. **Answers: A: 1.** 45, **2.** 18, **3.** 72, **4.** 17, **5.** 4, **B: 1.** +71, **2.** +15, **3.** –8, **4.** +98, **5.** –54.

(p92) MIDWORTHY SCHOOL'S EASTER FAYRE — PRACTICE EXERCISE

Learning outcomes
- **Identify and use appropriate operations (including combinations of operations) to solve word problems involving numbers and quantities** based on 'real life' money using one or more steps.
- Develop calculator skills and use a calculator effectively.
- Check with the inverse operation when using a calculator.

Lesson content
'Real life' problems using all four operations and involving both single and multi-step calculations. Encourage mental calculation and let them use calculators with their memory facility. Use inverse operations when checking with calculators.

Setting the homework
The Easter Fayre provides a follow-up of the lesson material.

Back at school
Mark the work. Discuss the mental strategies in question 1 and the ways they used calculator memory in question 2. **Answers: 1a.** 675, 575, 775, 800, 850, 625. Book token – Mr Evans, Fruit – Jenny Bates, Biscuits – Dave Goss, **1b.** £30, **1c.** £20.75, **2.** £265.37.

(p93) CONVERSIONS — PRACTICE EXERCISE

Learning outcomes
- **Identify and use appropriate operations to solve word problems involving quantities** based on measures.
- **Solve a problem by extracting and interpreting data in tables.**
- Know rough equivalents of oz. and g, in. and cm.
- Check with an inverse operation when using a calculator.

Lesson content
Explore temperature conversions with symbols (°C and °F). Build up flow charts showing how to calculate these conversions.

Setting the homework
Explain that the children are going to convert measures, using tables and calculations, as a follow-up from the lesson.

Back at school
Go through the questions. Discuss their 'can you say why?' answers. **Answers: 1a.** 85g, **b.** 227g, **c.** 396g, **d.** 680g. Check answers **a.** 84g, **b.** 224g, **c.** 392g, **d.** 672g, all based on 1oz is 28g, **2a.** 8oz, **b.** 12oz, **c.** 21oz, **3a.** 5.08, 12.7, 30.48, 91.44, **b(i).** 177.8mm (178mm), **b(ii).** 457.2mm (457mm), **c.** 12 inches = 1 foot, 36 inches = 1 yard.

(p94) FOREIGN CURRENCY — PRACTICE EXERCISE

Learning outcomes
- **Identify and use appropriate operations (including combinations of operations to solve word problems** including converting pounds to foreign currency.
- **Solve a problem by representing and extracting data in tables.**
- **Multiply and divide decimals mentally by 10 or 100.**
- Round a decimal to the nearest whole number.
- Develop calculator skills and use a calculator effectively.

Lesson content
Discuss currency exchange rates and why they might be needed, e.g. holidaying abroad. Draw up tables, for example, for French francs, showing the number of francs for £1, £2, £5, £10 and £100. Provide problems using various currencies.

Setting the homework
The homework provides further practice of the lesson content.

Back at school
Mark the questions with them and discuss their strategies. **Answers: 1a.** 1.47, 14.7, 147, 1470, **b.** 2.15, 21.5, 215, 2150, **2.** 294, **3.** 430 Canadian dollars (or 322 dollars 50 cents), **4a.** 5 950 pesetas, **b.** £22.12, **5.** Belgium (£306.50).

(p95) FACTORS AND PRIMES — INVESTIGATION

Learning outcomes
- Recognise prime numbers to at least 20.
- Solve mathematical problems, generalise and predict.
- Use tests of divisibility.
- Develop calculator skills and use a calculator effectively.

Lesson content
Investigate the statement, 'All square numbers have an odd number of factors', using a pair of factors approach, e.g. 64, 1 x 64, 2 x 32, 4 x 16, 8 x 8 giving 7 factors – an odd number. Let the children use a 100 square to develop prime numbers, i.e. dot all the multiples of 2 except 2 itself, dot all the multiples of 3 except 3 itself, then 4, 5 etc. Ask what they notice, e.g. All the multiples of 4 are already dotted because they are all multiples of 2. The numbers left without dots are the prime numbers but this still leaves a problem regarding 1. This is dealt with by the definition on the homework sheet but you may want to discuss this in the lesson.

Setting the homework
The homework revises and develops the lesson content.

Back at school
Discuss the various strategies used in the investigations. **Answers: 1.** 48 1, 2, 3, 4, 6, 8, 12, 16, 24, 48, **2a.** 16, 49, 121, 169, 225. **b.** They are all square numbers. **3.** No, **4.** 2, 3, 5, 7, 11, 13, 17, 19, 23, 29, 31, 37, 41, 43, 47, 53, 59, 61, 67, 71, 73, 79, 83, 89, 97, 101, 103, 107, 109, 113.

p96 FACTORISING AND PRIME FACTORS
PRACTICE EXERCISE

Learning outcomes
- Recognise prime numbers.
- Factorise numbers to 100 into prime factors.

Lesson content
Introduce the idea of factorising a number i.e. express it as a product of its factors. 40 could be 10 x 4 or 5 x 2 x 4 etc. Go on to factorise using prime factors only. A prime factor is a factor which is a prime number. 30 could be expressed as 5 x 3 x 2. All three numbers are prime. Give practice of these ideas.

Setting the homework
Read through the questions and sort out any problems.

Back at school
Ask individual children to supply answers.
Answers: 1a. and **b.** 21 1, 3, 7, 21 – 23 prime 1, 23 – 25 1, 5, 25 – 27 1, 3, 9, 27 – 29 prime 1, 29 – 31 prime 1, 31 – 33 1, 3, 11, 33 – 35 1, 5, 7, 35, **2.** Various answers including for **a.** 6 x 4, 8 x 3, **b.** 7 x 4, 7 x 2 x 2, **c.** 9 x 5, 15 x 3, **d.** 27 x 2, 9 x 3 x 2, **e.** 38 x 2, 19 x 4, **3.** 8 = 2 x 2 x 2, 9 = 3 x 3, 10 = 5 x 2, 12 = 3 x 2 x 2, 14 = 7 x 2, 15 = 5 x 3, 16 = 2 x 2 x 2 x 2, 18 = 3 x 3 x 2.

p97 BIG WHEEL
GAMES AND PUZZLES

Learning outcomes
- Recognise squares of numbers to at least 12 x 12.
- Factorise numbers.
- **Use a fraction as an 'operator' to find fractions of numbers.**
- Use known number facts to consolidate mental addition/subtraction, multiplication and division.

Lesson content
Introduce square roots from, for example [ ] x [ ] = 25, five squared is 25 and the square root of 25 is 5. Make the point that squaring and finding the square root are inverses. Use 'trial and improvement' strategies to find square roots using a calculator e.g. with a target of 324, 20^2 is 400, 16^2 is 256, 18^2 is 324, so 18 is the square root of 324. Set questions involving finding square roots with and without calculators e.g. square root of 64, 289 and for the more able 10. Introduce the √ sign.

Setting the homework
Ensure the children understand each sentence starts with the central number.

Back at school
Go through the answers. Go on to try the Big Wheels produced by the children. **Answers:** Centre number 16, is ⅛th of 128, can be factorised to become 2 x 2 x 2 x 2, is the square root of 256, is the difference between 1040 and 1056 (or 1024), is 9 less than 5 squared.

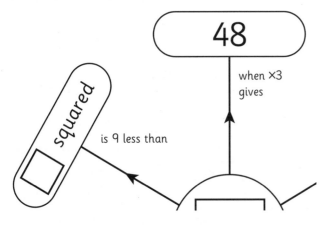

48

when ×3 gives

squared

is 9 less than

p98 PATHWAYS
GAMES AND PUZZLES

Learning outcome
- **Multiply and divide decimals mentally by 10 or 100, and integers by 1000.**

Lesson context
Discuss the effect of using x10, x100 and x1000 on integers. Follow this with decimal inputs. Next try ÷10 followed by ÷100 and ÷1000. Try combining functions, e.g. ÷10 and then ÷100 is equivalent to ÷1000. Provide examples using all six functions including for example 9 ÷ [ ] = 0.09.

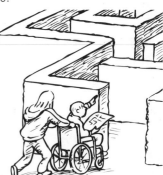

Setting the homework
The homework gives practice of the lesson content in puzzle form. Make sure that they understand the pathways layout.

Back at school
There are many solutions. Let the children check each other's work including the pathways brought to school.

p99 MAKE IT REAL
PRACTICE EXERCISE

Learning outcomes
- Round a number with two decimal places to the nearest tenth or whole number.
- **Solve a problem by interpreting data in tables.**
- Develop calculator skills and use a calculator effectively.

Lesson context
Discuss the contexts in which tables of large whole numbers are found, e.g. mountain heights, river lengths. Approximate the numbers, first ordering them and then rounding to a suitable degree of accuracy. Round decimals to both the nearest tenth and to the nearest whole number. Try some division calculations which need rounding, using calculators. Emphasise 'real life' situations in the lesson.

Setting the homework
Emphasise realistic suggestions in questions 1 and 4.

Back at school
Discuss the children's ideas and the answers to questions 1 and 4. **Answers: 2a.** 12.7, **b.** 113.5, **c.** 454.1, **3a.** 275, **b.** 1040, **c.** 5.

p100 MULTI-HEX
PRACTICE EXERCISE

Learning outcomes
- Understand and use the relationships between the four operations, and the principles (not the names) of the arithmetic laws.
- Use related facts and doubling and halving.
- Use factors.
- Use closely related facts.

Lesson context
Explore the children's own written methods of multiplication of two digits by two digits, having first estimated the result. Go on to the multiplication of three-digit by two-digit numbers.

Setting the homework
Talk about the various strategies they used. Emphasise that all working should accompany the homework sheet.

Back at school
Discuss the results and ask individuals to talk about the strategy they used. **Answers:** 16 x 25 = 400, 25 x 19 = 475, 19 x 34 = 646, 34 x 17 = 578, 17 x 43 = 731.

p101 WHAT'S THE COST?
PRACTICE EXERCISE

Learning outcome
* **Extend written methods to long multiplication of a three-digit by a two-digit integer.**

Lesson context
Work with the children to produce the standard written method of long multiplication from strategies developed previously.

Setting the homework
Tell the class to read the sheet carefully and ask any questions. Calculators should not be used. They should use paper for calculations and write answers in the spaces on the sheet.

Back at school
Discuss the question and ask individuals for their answers.
Answers: Full cost of two coaches @ £56.50 each is £113. Acme's discount cost (£1.45 x 72) is £104.40. Entrance fee for 64 children is £87.04, for eight adults is £25.60, making a total of £112.64. 37 lunches @ £2.26 is £83.62. Money to be collected by Mrs Jacks: £104.40 + £112.64 + £83.62 = £300.66. Acme discount £8.60.

p102 TIMED DIVISIONS
TIMED PRACTICE EXERCISE

Learning outcomes
* **Extend written methods to** division of HTU by TU.
* Develop calculator skills and use a calculator effectively.

Lesson context
Work with the class using multiplication and subtraction to solve division problems, leading to a written method. For example, 595 ÷ 17 may be seen as; 'I think it's over 30', 17 multiplied by 30 is 510, that leaves 85. 17 multiplied by 5 is 85. Answer 35.

Setting the homework
Tell the children to do their working on rough paper and write the answers on the sheet. They must bring both sheets back to school.

Back at school
Give answers and question individuals about the time taken to answer each set of questions. **Answers: Set 1 – a.** 23, **b.** 34, **c.** 47, **d.** 35. **Set 2 – a.** 38, **b.** 17, **c.** 27, **d.** 24.

p103 EXPLORING NUMBERS
INVESTIGATION

Learning outcomes
* Consolidate all strategies from previous year.
* Develop calculator skills and use a calculator effectively.
* Choose and use appropriate number operations to solve problems, and appropriate ways of calculating.
* Explain methods and reasoning.
* Make and investigate a general statement about familiar numbers or shapes by finding examples that satisfy it.

Lesson context
Try an investigation involving squaring any two consecutive numbers and finding the difference between their squares. The class work in pairs to produce a report. Encourage a systematic approach. Trying 12 with 22, 22 with 32 and so on, leading to 'the sum of the two chosen numbers is equal to the difference of their squares'.

Setting the homework
Read the homework sheet and explain that you want individuals to report their findings under the same headings as the lesson.

Back at school
Display the reports and ask individuals to share their findings.
Answers: Various. They will lead to the final conclusion that the difference between the square of the middle number, and the first and third numbers multiplied together, is always the square of the initial difference between the three numbers.

p104 GETTING CLOSE
TIMED PRACTICE EXERCISE

Learning outcomes
* Understand the relationships between the four operations.
* Use the relationship between multiplication and division.
* Use known number facts and place value to consolidate mental multiplication and division.

Lesson context
The children play a game in which they give whole number estimates of division of three-digit numbers by two-digit numbers. Each estimate is checked using a calculator, and the player with the closest estimate scores a point.

Setting the homework
Remind the class that this is a timed homework so only write the estimate and the time taken for each question.

Back at school
Give answers and discuss individual strategies.
Answers: 1. 8, 18, 13, 23, 24, 19, **2a.** 18, **b.** 12, **c.** 9, **d.** 14, **e.** 15, **f.** 6.

p105 MIXED AND MATCHED
PRACTICE EXERCISE

Learning outcomes
* Change a fraction to the equivalent mixed number.
* **Reduce a fraction to its simplest form by cancelling common fractions.**
* Recognise relationships between fractions.

Lesson context
Provide activities involving changing improper fractions to mixed numbers and finding the differences between improper fractions and whole numbers. For example, $\frac{17}{6}$ and 3. Ask for strategies e.g. '$\frac{17}{6}$ is $2\frac{5}{6}$ which is $\frac{1}{6}$ less than 3'. Follow this with questions involving reducing fractions to their simplest form by cancelling common factors in the numerator and denominator.

Setting the homework
The homework follows up the work of the lesson.

Back at school
Mark the questions with the children. **Answers:** 2 with e, 3 with f, 4 with b, 5 with d, 6 with a, **7a.** $\frac{3}{4}$, **b.** $2\frac{3}{5}$, **c.** $\frac{1}{6}$, **8.** $\frac{29}{6}$, **9a.** 100, **b.** $\frac{1}{2}$, **c.** $\frac{10}{12}$ [or an equivalent fraction], $3\frac{1}{3}$.

p106 TRIANGULAR GROWTH
PRACTICE EXERCISE

Learning outcomes
* **Solve simple problems involving ratio and proportion.**
* Recognise number sequences, such as sequences of square numbers.

Lesson context
Remind the children of the previous work on ratio and proportion, where ratio compares part to part and proportion compares a part to a whole. Produce ratio and proportion questions for the children to try such as mixing ingredients, or tiling an area with a two-colour tile pattern.

Setting the homework
Make sure that the questions are understood and suggest that a number sequence may develop from the triangular growth.

Back at school
Work through the sheet and develop the square number sequence from the triangular growth i.e. length of side 2, number of triangles 4 (2^2); length of side 4, number of triangles 16 (4^2) etc.
Answers: 1a. 4, **b.** $\frac{1}{4}$, **2.** 1 to 4, **3.** 4 in 5 or $\frac{4}{5}$, **4.** 36, **5a.** 1 to 9, **b.** 4 to 9, **6.** 1 to 16.

p107 USING PERCENTAGE
PRACTICE EXERCISE

Learning outcomes
- **Understand percentage as the number of parts in every 100.**
- **Find simple percentages of small whole number quantities.**
- **Identify and use appropriate operations (including combinations of operations) to solve word problems involving numbers and quantities based on 'real life', money or measures, using one or more steps.**
- **Explain methods and reasoning.**

Lesson context
Link percentage ideas to proportion. For example, in a class, if 55% are girls, 45% must be boys. Talk about relationships with common fractions and decimals, e.g. 37 out of 100 = $\frac{37}{100}$ or 0.37 out of 1 or 37%. Give the children some practice using these equivalences and apply percentages to 'real world' situations, involving data, money and measures.

Setting the homework
This follows up the lesson with examples using percentages.

Back at school
Mark the work with the children asking them how they tackled individual questions. **Answers: 1a.** £1500, **b.** £12.00, **c.** £1.60, **d.** 2.5kg, **e.** 1.5km, **f.** 10cl, **2a.** 12%, **b(i).** 27, **(ii).** 23, **3.** £16.00, **4a.** 86%, 76%, 62%, 58%, **b.** Serena and James, **c.** 46, 42, 33, 27.

p108 TIMING TV
INVESTIGATION

Learning outcomes
- **Understand percentage as the number of parts in every 100.**
- **Solve a problem by** representing **and interpreting data in tables.**
- Develop calculator skills and use a calculator effectively.

Lesson context
Talk about proportions and percentages of a given set of data, e.g. a class shoe size survey. Build up a 'rectangular graph' to scale from the data, e.g.

Sizes	less than 4	4	5	6	greater than 6
	2 (7%)	9 (30%)	10 (33%)	6 (20%)	3 (10%)

Discuss the graph noting that it shows all the data (ie,100%), with the number of children wearing particular shoe sizes represented in the correct proportion and percentage to scale.

Setting the homework
Discuss the survey, bringing out the fact that each number of minutes quoted is part of the total time (270 minutes), and that they can choose their own 'type of programme' categories.

Back at school
Draw up the BBC1 table on the board and complete it. Discuss the children's surveys, identifying the different 'type of programme' categories needed and the fact that some percentages do not total 100%, and so on.
Answers: 11%, 19%, 13%, 9%, 15%.

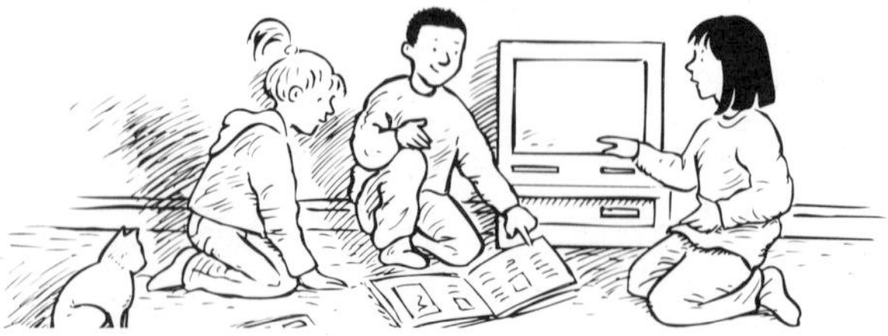

p109 NETBALL RESULTS
PRACTICE EXERCISE

Learning outcomes
- **Understand percentage as the number of parts in every 100.**
- Express fractions as percentages.
- **Solve a problem by** representing **and interpreting data in graphs.**
- **Use a protractor to measure** and draw **angles to the nearest degree.**
- Develop calculator skills and use calculator effectively.

Lesson context
Prepare a rectangular graph and a pie chart to show the same survey information using common fractions such as: 'Smoking habits of adults'. Discuss the two graphs. $\frac{1}{3}$ smoke, $\frac{1}{2}$ have smoked but have stopped, $\frac{1}{6}$ have never smoked. Explain how the 'slices' of the pie represent the data (fractional parts of 100% and of the 360° of a circle). Discuss how1% is represented by about 4°. Compile data for children to use for pie charts.

Setting the homework
Discuss the sheet, ensuring the questions are understood.

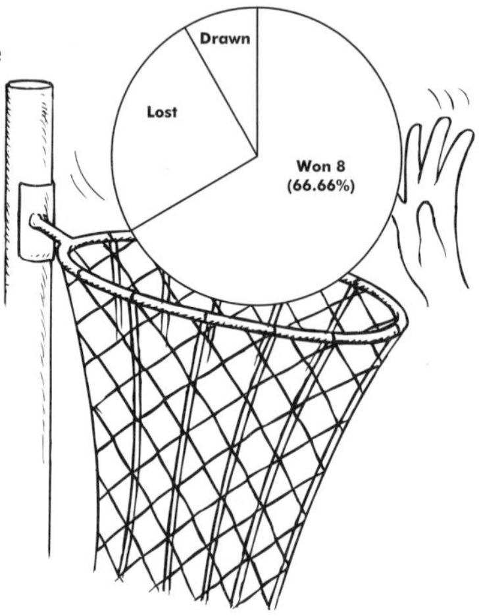

Back at school
Give the answers and help individuals who experienced problems. For example, in calculating and/or drawing the correct angles on the pie chart.
Answers: 1. Lynside Primary School netball results: lost 3, 25%; drew 1, 8.33%;
2. Henwick Primary School netball results: won 50%; lost $33\frac{1}{3}$%, drew 16.66%.

p110 DECIGRID
GAMES AND PUZZLES

Learning outcomes
- Recognise the equivalence between the decimal and common fraction forms of one half, one quarter, one eighth and one tenth.
- Recognise relationships between fractions.
- Extend written methods to:
  column addition and subtraction of numbers involving decimals
  short multiplication and division of numbers involving decimals.

Lesson context
The lesson centres around the Fibonacci Sequence 0, 1, 1, 2, 3, 5, 8…, with each number being the sum of the previous two numbers, and Fibonacci Fractions with their equivalents $\frac{1}{1}$ = 1, $\frac{2}{1}$ = 2, $\frac{3}{2}$ = 1.5, $\frac{5}{3}$ = 1.6666, $\frac{8}{5}$ = 1.6 etc. Let the children use an investigative approach with calculators to assist them. Discuss the decimal results drawing comments from them such as, 'they are all between 1 and 2', or 'the decimal numbers are moving to around 1.1618'.

Setting the homework
The sheet explores decimal equivalents of common fractions. Make sure that the children understand the Decigrid puzzle.

Back at school
Ask the children for their answers, remembering that alternative solutions are possible for the Decigrid questions.
Answers: 1a. 0.25, 0.375, 0.5, 0.625, 0.875, **b.** 0.4, 0.6, 0.8, **c.** 0.1, 0.3, 0.7, 0.9, **2a.** answers various, **b.** 0.075, **c.** 1.5 is 0.875 less than 2.375 i.e. $\frac{7}{8}$ less.

p111 STEPPING STONES AGAIN   INVESTIGATION

Learning outcome
- Use the language associated with probability to discuss events, including those with equally likely outcomes.

Lesson context
Divide the class into three groups with 8 to 12 children in each group. Use a 'Stepping stones' game to explore ideas of probability. In each group the children are split into two teams and stepping stones are made or drawn, as shown below.

Each team decides which totals will be most frequent when the numbers rolled on two cubic dice are added together. They are then given seven counters to place on the numbers of their choice, no more than three counters on any stepping stone. The teams take turns to roll the dice. If the total is the same as one of their 'stepping stones' on which there is a counter or counters, then they can remove one of the counters and place it on the other side of the river. The winning team is the first to get all their counters across the river. When the game is finished, discuss the placing of the counters and follow this by analysing the number of ways of making each number. (1 no way; 2, one way.; 3, two ways and so on up to 12, one way).

Setting the homework
This homework practises the work on probability covered in the lesson. Read through the sheet and briefly discuss some of the numbers it is possible to make.

Back at school
Ask individuals to give their results to question 1, and discuss questions 2 and 3. **Answers: 1.** 1, 2, 3, 4, 5, 6, 8, 9, 10, 12, 15, 16, 18, 20, 24, 25, 30, 36.

p112 GRAPHS FROM ORDERED PAIRS   PRACTICE EXERCISE

Learning outcomes
- **Solve a problem by** representing **extracting and interpreting data in charts, tables and graphs.**
- **Read and plot co-ordinates in all four quadrants.**

Lesson context
Use the first quadrant of a prepared four-quadrant graph to explore the equation $x + y = 8$. Ask for ordered pairs which satisfy the equation, (consider both whole numbers and decimals) and ask what the graph will look like. Extend these ideas to the other quadrants. The children then work in pairs plotting other equations such as $x + y = 10$.

Setting the homework
Read the sheet, reminding the children of the work covered in the lesson. Give out the graph paper.

Back at school
Give the results to questions 1 and 2 and display some of the graphs. **Answers: 1a.** 2, **b.** 12, **c.** –3, **d.** –5, **e.** 9, **f.** 18.

2.	x	–5	–4	–3	–2	–1	0	1	2	3	4	5
	y	14	13	12	11	10	9	8	7	6	5	4

3.	x	–4	–3	–2	–1	0	1	2	3	4	5	6	7	8
	y	2	3	4	5	6	7	8	9	10	11	12	13	14

p113 NAME THAT GRAPH!   PRACTICE EXERCISE

Learning outcomes
- **Solve a problem by** representing **extracting and interpreting data in charts, tables and graphs.**
- **Read and plot co-ordinates in all four quadrants.**

Lesson context
With five pairs of co-ordinates, (1,1), (2,4), (3,9), (4,16) and (5,25) marked on a prepared four-quadrant graph ask for their relationship and the equation of the graph formed ($y = x2$). Children draw the graph in the first quadrant only. Discuss the results and ask individuals to predict the path of the graph in the other quadrants. Let the children complete their graph using calculators, with sign change keys to help when calculating negative co-ordinates.

Setting the homework
Remind the children that they will need to look for a relationship between the 'x' and 'y' co-ordinates each time, in order to find the equations of the given lines and curves. However, an equation can be formed when the 'x' or 'y' values are constant, for example, when the line is parallel to the 'x' axis and every point along the line has a 'y' co-ordinate of 6 for example. The equation of this line is $y = 6$.

Back at school
Ask individuals for their results and discuss any problems that have arisen. **Answers: a.** $y = x$, **b.** $y = -x$, **c.** $y = x - 7$ or $x - y = 7$, **d.** $y = -2$, **e.** $y = x2 \div 2$, **f.** $x = -7$.

p114 FIND THE TRIANGLES   GAMES AND PUZZLES

Learning outcomes
- Make shapes with increasing accuracy.
- **Use a protractor to measure and draw acute and obtuse angles to the nearest degree.**
- Solve mathematical problems, recognise and explain patterns and relationships, generalise and predict. Suggest extensions asking, 'What if...?'

Lesson context
Give each group a set of regular polygons, and a large sheet of paper. Ask the groups to select a polygon, and draw round it. Now use the original polygons as a template and see how many polygons it is possible to draw around the starter polygon, sharing an edge with it. Record this number. Now choose other polygons, recording the number in the layer each time. What do the children notice? Encourage them to construct other polygons to test their predictions.

Setting the homework
Read through the homework sheet ensuring the children understand what is meant by a diagonal. Remind them that you will be asking for the method they used to find the result.

Back at school
Ask individuals for their answer and the method they used. Discuss other methods. **Answer:** 11 triangles.

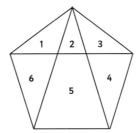

Triangles with...		
1 region	2 regions	3 regions
1	1,2	1,2,3
2	2,3	
3	3,4	
4	2,5	
6	6,1	

 **p115** WHERE IS IT NOW?   PRACTICE EXERCISE

Learning outcomes
- Recognise where a shape will be after a rotation through 90° about one of its vertices.
- Make shapes with increasing accuracy.
- **Use a protractor to measure and draw acute and obtuse angles to the nearest degree.**

Lesson context
Select one child and ask how they would rotate an equilateral triangle through 90° anti-clockwise about its vertex. The children work in pairs and accurately construct a rectangle and label a vertex P. The rectangle is rotated anti-clockwise through 90° and the image is drawn. This activity is continued until the rectangle is back in its original position.

Setting the homework
Read the sheet with the children and remind them that sharp pencils and accurate rulers and protractors are required.

Back at school
Ask individuals for the answers to question 1 and display the constructions for question 2. **Answers: a.** 90° anti-clockwise, **b.** 40° clockwise, **c.** 60° anti-clockwise.

 **p116** FOLLOWING INSTRUCTIONS   PRACTICE EXERCISE

Learning outcomes
- Recognise where a shape will be after a rotation.
- Recognise where a shape will be after two translations.

Lesson context
Introduce translation as a type of movement and ask the children to draw a simple shape and repeatedly translate and rotate the shape, to produce a pattern.

Setting the homework
Read the sheet carefully, ensuring the children understand the instructions.

Back at school
Discuss and display the images produced. Answer: The original shape can be translated to produce the final image.

 **p117** HOW DOES IT GET THERE?   PRACTICE EXERCISE

Learning outcomes
- Recognise where a shape will be after two translations.
- **Read and plot co-ordinates in all four quadrants.**

Lesson context
The lesson centres around the relationship between the co-ordinates of a triangle when it is translated on a four-quadrant graph and its image. Go on to ask one of each pair of children to draw another simple shape, and give the relationship which will allow their partner to draw the image.

Setting the homework
Ensure that the children appreciate the original shape is shown as solid lines and its image is shown as broken lines.

Back at school
Discuss the ways in which the quadrilateral may have been translated. **Answer:** The quadrilateral has been translated **1)** into the second quadrant, having co-ordinates (–6,1), (–6,2), (–5,4), (–4,1), (subtract 7 from the original 'x' co-ordinates). The next step involved translating the quadrilateral into the third quadrant, (–6,–5), (–6,–4), (–5,–2), (–4,–5), (subtract 6 from the 'y' co-ordinates of the second quadrant image). **Or 2)** The quadrilateral has been translated into the fourth quadrant, having co-ordinates (1,–5), (1,–4), (2,–2), (3,–5), (subtract 6 from the original 'y' co-ordinates), followed finally by translating the quadrilateral into the third quadrant, (subtract 7 from the 'x' co-ordinates of the fourth quadrant image).

 **p118** COUNTING DIAGONALS   INVESTIGATION

Learning outcomes
- Explain methods and reasoning, orally and in writing.
- Make and investigate a general statement about familiar numbers or shapes by finding examples that satisfy it. Develop from explaining a generalised relationship in words to expressing it in a formula.

Lesson context
The lesson centres around rolling a circle around different polygons and observing the shape and length of the path made by the centre of the circle each time. Results are discussed and a formula is produced, initially in words. 'It doesn't matter what shape the polygon is, the length of the path is always the sum of the perimeter of the polygon and the circumference of the circle'. This leads to, $p = s + c$, where p is the path, s is the perimeter of the shape, and c is the circumference of the circle.

Setting the homework
Make sure that the children understand the difference between drawing (a) and (b). It might be helpful to draw another circle and mark six points, working together to see how many straight lines are possible without forming any triangles (7).

Back at school
Ask an individual to read their report as a basis for discussion.

Answers:

Number of points	1	2	3	4	5	6	7	8	9	10	11	12	13	14	15	16	17	18
Number of lines drawn	0	1	2	4	5	7	8	10	11	13	14	16	17	19	20	22	23	25

Many statements are possible such as, 'The number of lines increases by two every time there is an even number of points'. 'The odd number sequence of points increases by three each time, so does the even number sequence'.

p119 TUG O' WAR   PRACTICE EXERCISE

Learning outcomes
- Use, read and write kilograms including its abbreviation kg.
- **Solve a problem by** representing **extracting and interpreting data in charts, tables and graphs,** frequency tables and bar charts with grouped discrete data.
- Find the median and mean of a set of data.
- Develop calculator skills and use a calculator effectively.

Lesson context
In groups, the children estimate, measure and record their heights to the nearest centimetre. Discuss the estimates. Prepare a 'Class Heights' chart and record each child's height. Consider the range and mean height of the class. Build a new chart with heights in order. Find the mode and median and compare these with the mean. The children should create a frequency table using grouped data, and draw a bar chart.

Setting the homework
The homework follows up the lesson.

Back at school
Mark the work together, fill in the frequency table and draw the graph on the board. Discuss 1d and 4. **Answers: 1a.** 683kg, 685kg, **b.** 98kg, 98kg, **c.** 97kg, 101kg. **2.** Kyford, 0,1,1,3,1,1. Evalmoor, 1,0,2,0,3,1. Total number of men, 1,1,3,3,4,2.

p120 CORA'S 100cm² PUZZLE
GAMES AND PUZZLES

Learning outcomes
* **Calculate the area of simple shapes.**
* Solve mathematical puzzles.

Lesson context
Fix the area of a rectangle and observe different perimeters. Let the children try various possibilities and record their results in a table. Try other areas such as 36cm², 64cm², sketching each rectangle or using graph paper where feasible. Draw conclusions such as, for rectangles with a fixed area, many different perimeters are possible. The smallest is given by a square, whilst thin rectangles have very large perimeters.

Setting the homework
Make sure that the children understand Cora's puzzle and the challenge. Don't give too much away. Some strategies are suggested to the helper.

Back at school
Ask the children how they tackled the puzzle. Photocopy your solution and distribute it around the class. Give out the children's puzzles for others to try.

Answer:

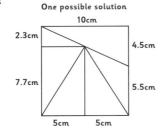

One possible solution

p121 AROUND THE WORLD
MATHS TO SHARE

Learning outcome
* Appreciate different times around the world.

Lesson context
Explain, using a globe, that the earth rotates through 360° in 24 hours giving 15° turn in each hour. Explore Greenwich Mean Time (GMT) and that places in the world are a number of hours ahead or behind it. Introduce time zones and show them on a world map. Some countries adjust times to suit their boundaries. Give them questions based on this, e.g. Samoa is 11 hours behind GMT. *When it is 12 noon in London, what time is it in Samoa?* Use an atlas to help you decide why Portugal uses GMT. Discuss British Summer Time (BST).

Setting the homework
The homework gives practice of the work covered in the lesson. Provide an atlas for those children who do not have one and make sure they understand how to use the information given in the international codes section of the telephone directory.

Back at school
Ask individuals how they tackled the Time Zone Line question. Discuss some of the unusual facts such as India and South Australia use half hours, or that there are very few places with −11 (mainly sea).

p122 CONVERTING MEASURES
PRACTICE EXERCISE

Learning outcomes
* **Identify and use appropriate operations to solve word problems involving quantities** based on measures.
* Know (and use) equivalents (of pounds to kg, gallons to l).
* **Solve a problem by interpreting data** in diagrams and graphs.
* Develop calculator skills (including checks) and use a calculator effectively.

Lesson context
Give the children activities which involve conversion from imperial to metric units using cooking recipes. Use temperature conversions, including a conversion graph, using the formula, $°C = (°F − 32) \times 5 \div 9$.

Setting the homework
Remind the children about conversion line diagrams as you read through the questions with them. Discuss accuracy when reading scales, for example, when using a ruler.

Back at school
Work through the sheet with the children. **Answers: 1.** 2.2lbs, **2a.** 1.1lb, 7.7lb, **b.** 8.8lb, **3.** about 4.5l, **5.** 6.6 gallons, **6.** £3.69, **7.** Mrs Symes, 8.5l.

p123 TARGET BASKETBALL
GAMES AND PUZZLES

Learning outcome
* Use known number facts and place value to consolidate mental addition, subtraction, multiplication and division.

Lesson context
Write four decimal numbers on the board. Ask the children to mentally add any two of them (six possibilities). Go on to ask for additions of three and then all four numbers. Then let them work in pairs on four new decimal numbers. Finally, try four numbers, written in ascending order, using subtractions. No negative number answers are allowed. Jottings can be used, but not vertical calculations.

Setting the homework
Explain Target basketball, emphasising that it is a mental activity, as in the lesson, but now involving all four operations.

Back at school
Go through each basket number, inviting children to contribute suggestions. Announce the basket points winner.

p124 TROUBLE-SHOOTING
PRACTICE EXERCISE

Learning outcomes
* **Identify and use appropriate operations (including combinations of operations) to solve word problems** based on 'real life', money, using one or more steps and calculating percentages such as VAT and discount.
* Develop calculator skills and use a calculator effectively.

Lesson context
Talk about invoices and write a simple example on the board which includes VAT. Discuss VAT and show how to calculate it using a calculator. Ask the children the meaning of the word 'discount'. Give individual children some invoice questions.

Setting the homework
Trouble-shooting gives further practice of the use of invoices.

Back at school
Using calculators go through each question to find the errors. **Answers: 1.** Bloomsgrove Chairs, £433.08. Total: £987.08. **2.** VAT £15.37. Total due: £103.22. **3.** Discount £20.37. Total with discount: £115.45, VAT £20.20. Total due: £135.65.

p125 CRACK IT!
GAMES AND PUZZLES

Learning outcomes
- Solve mathematical problems or puzzles, recognise and explain patterns and relationships.
- Recognise and extend number sequences.

Lesson context
Work out a simple code using one function, for example x4. Write a message using the code. Show how to lay out the alphabet (as shown on the homework sheet) and start to solve the code with the children. Let them complete it and write their own message for a partner. The children now go on to invent their own code using two functions, e.g.1 followed by x5 and write a message using it for their partner to crack.

Setting the homework
Tell the children that Georgia's code is similar to those they have been creating.

Back at school
Ask individuals what they think the functions used were and invite them to tell the other children how they went about finding them. Let them try each other's messages. **Answer:** Functions used, x3 followed by –2.

.... so b is 4
.... so e is 13
.... so j is 28
.... so m is 37

p126 MULTIPLE PROBLEMS
PRACTICE EXERCISE

Learning outcomes
- Find simple common multiples.
- **Solve a problem by** representing **and interpreting data in diagrams.**

Lesson context
Work with the children on multiples of two numbers using a Venn diagram. Introduce the phrase 'common multiples' pointing out that they appear in the central (intersection) region. Include numbers which are not multiples of either number on the diagram (see homework sheet). Let the children draw other common multiple Venn diagrams. Ask questions such as: What is the lowest common multiple of 3 and 8? What is the common multiple of 3 and 8 which is nearest to 50?

Setting the homework
The homework follows directly from the lesson content.

Back at school
Build up the question 1 Venn diagram on the board and ask the children how they tackled the other questions.
Answers: 1a. multiples of 7; 7, 14, 21 (given), 28, 35 (given), 42, 49; multiples of 4, 4 (given), 8 (given), 12, 16, 20, 24, 32, 36, 40, 44, 48, 52, 60; multiples of 4 and 7, 28, 56 (given), b) 7 and 4 is 28, **2a.** 6, 12, 18, 24, **b.** various, **c.** 72.

p127 WHAT CAN YOU SAY?
INVESTIGATION

Learning outcomes
- Recognise multiples up to 10 x 10.
- Recognise prime numbers to at least 20.
- Recognise number sequences, such as the sequence of square numbers, or the sequence of triangular numbers.

Lesson context
Write on the board and investigate a 'stepping' sequence of numbers, for example:

```
1
2   3
3   5   6
4   7   9   10
5   9   12  14  15
```

Ask what they notice. 'The first column goes up in 1's, the second in 2's starting from 3, and so on.' 'The differences in each line decrease by 1 each time'. 'The end diagonal gives triangular numbers'. Let them extend the 'stepping' sequence. Try another 'stepping' sequence, e.g. column one, the counting numbers; column two, multiples of 2, column 3, multiples of 3.

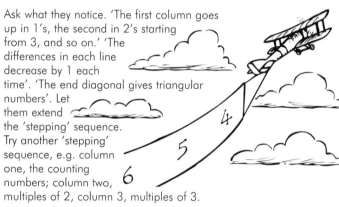

Setting the homework
The report should include each number separately and it should be as extensive as possible.

Back at school
Ask about the comments the children made for each number. Follow up with extension ideas such as, 'Two adjacent triangular numbers when added always give a square number'.

p128 WHAT'S THE DIFFERENCE?
INVESTIGATION

Learning outcomes
- Recognise and extend number sequences, such as the sequence of square numbers.
- Make and investigate a general statement about familiar numbers.
- Develop calculator skills and use a calculator effectively.

Lesson context
Make up cubes from Multilinks or similar kits (1, 8 and 27). Ask how many small cubes there are in each. Develop cubic numbers 1^3 (1), 2^3 (8), 3^3 (27) and so on. Let them extend the sequence using calculators. Ask, for example: What's the first cubic number greater than 500, 1 000, 10 000?

Setting the homework
Run through the sheet to ensure that the children understand the rows of differences they are to develop.

Back at school
Build up the difference patterns and conclusions on the board. **Answers: 1.** First row differences are the odd numbers from 3 to 19. Second row differences are all 2. Comments such as, 'At row 2 all the differences are the same (2)'. **2a.** 2, 8, 18, 32, 50, 72, 98, 128, 162, 200. **2b.** First row differences start at 6 and increase by 4 each time up to 38; second row differences are all 4. **2c.** This time the differences still stayed the same at row two, the difference number being 4. **3a.** 1, 8, 27, 64, 125, 216, 343, 512, 729, 1000. First row differences: 7, 19, 37, 61, 91, 127, 169, 217, 271. Second row differences: 12, 18. 24, 30, 36, 42, 48, 54. Third row differences are all 6. **3b.** The difference stayed the same at row three, the difference number being 6.

Name: _____

Up to a million

You will need: a pencil and some scrap paper.

1 a Arrange the digits 6, 8, 2, 5, 4 to
make the highest number you can.   _____

   b Write the number in words.   _____

   c Now make the lowest number
you can from the same digits.   _____

   d Write the number in words.

_____

2 a Is the number 28 830 nearer to 28 500 or 29 000?   _____

   b What is the difference between 28 830
and the answer you have given?   _____

3 Write the following numbers in figures:

   a two thousand and seventy.   _____

   b twenty-five thousand, six hundred and eighty.   _____

   c seven hundred and thirty thousand and ninety-six.   _____

4 Write down the number which is:

   a two hundred less than half a million.   _____

   b sixty thousand more than a quarter of a million.   _____

   c half way between three-quarters of a
million and a million.   _____

Dear Helper,

This activity is to help your child gain confidence using very large numbers and to know the value of each digit according to its position. Encourage them to use scrap paper to jot down their intermediate steps on the way to the answer.

Investigating really large numbers

You will need: a pencil, paper, a calculator and some sources of information which give large numbers. Try local newspapers or reference books such as *The Guinness Book of Records* or an atlas. Alternatively, use the Internet.

- Carry out a search for really large numbers. Here are some ideas. Use some of them, but think up your own as well.

What is the total population of North America?

How far is it to the Moon, or the Sun?

Carry out a house price survey using a local newspaper.

What is the difference between the price of the cheapest and most expensive three-bedroomed house?

Make a list showing the cost of properties above £120 000.

About how long are 'around the world' yacht races?

About how many birds are there in a King Penguin colony in Antarctica?

How many people visit all the various National Trust properties every year?

About how many single CDs are sold by top pop singers or bands?

Dear Helper,

The suggestions on this sheet indicate a few of the uses of large numbers in the world. You can help by searching for some source materials together. Assure your child that they do not have to work on all the ideas shown. Your child's own ideas may be better.

CALCULATIONS UNDERSTANDING × AND ÷

Name:

Crossing the river

You will need: some paper and coloured pencils
or felt-tipped pens.

reed bank

- Cross the river by moving one stone horizontally, vertically or
  diagonally each time.

    To do this you must use all the digits 5, 3, 7, 6 each time,
    together with +, −, ×, ÷ and ( ) as often as you need.

    Some moves might not be possible.

- Mark your path in a colour and record the calculation you use
  each time.

- Find as many ways as you can to cross the river starting from
  anywhere along the reed bank. Show each path in a
  different colour.

PHOTOCOPIABLE

Dear Helper,

Your child will have been using the relationships between +, −, × and ÷ and brackets in class. Make sure
that they understand and remember that calculations inside brackets should always be done first.
Successful calculations should be recorded on a separate sheet of paper.

Name:

Estimate!

You will need: a partner to play the game with and a calculator. You will also need eight counters each of two different colours (5p and 2p coins will do).

141	204	272	76	476
133	216	423	430	774
162	258	344	270	378
612	235	171	340	486

- Take turns to choose two of these numbers to multiply together on your calculator:

 7   47   9   19   5   86   54   4   3

- Cover the answer on the grid with one of your counters.

- The winner is the first player to cover four squares in a line – horizontally, vertically or diagonally.

Dear Helper,

Estimation is a vital skill and this activity is to help your child estimate the result of mentally multiplying a two-digit number by a single digit. Encourage your child to estimate the result before entering any numbers into the calculator. Your child can check roughly what the answer will be and whether it will let them cover the square needed to help produce a successful line of four.

Using grids to multiply

You will need: a pencil, and a calculator.

- Use the grid method to solve these multiplications.
  Each time estimate first. The first one has been done for you.

1 527 × 6

×	5	2	7
6	3 000	120	42

3 000 + 120 + 42 = 3 162
_____

2 384 × 27

_____

3 678 × 53

_____

4 1 392 × 8

_____

5 2 087 × 76

_____

- Check your answers using a calculator.

- Now choose two of the questions and write 'real world'
  situations for them. Continue on the back of this sheet if you
  need more space to write.

Dear Helper,

The calculations on this sheet are to help your child estimate, and then find the answer to, multiplications of a large number by a single digit using a grid method. This method is an introduction to short multiplication of larger numbers.

Name:

Cross-number

You will need: a pencil and some paper.

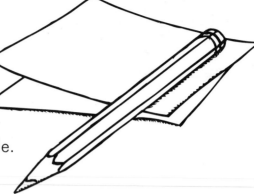

DO NOT USE A CALCULATOR

- Use the clues below to solve this cross-number puzzle.

  Remember to estimate first.

Clues

Across

1   1845×3

3   1798×4

4   986×7

5   $[\ \ ] \div 17 = 5$

Down

1   1269×4

2   837×6

Dear Helper,

The cross-number calculations involve the multiplication of two-, three- and four-digit numbers by a single digit. Encourage your child to estimate first and then do a written calculation on a sheet of paper, before entering the result on the puzzle. Hide the calculator!

100 MATHS HOMEWORK ACTIVITIES • YEAR 6 TERM 1

Name:

Divisions

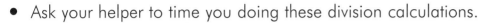

You will need: some paper, a pencil, a ruler and a watch with a seconds hand.

- Ask your helper to time you doing these division calculations.

- Use a sheet of paper to do your written calculations and record your answers on this sheet.

- Try each set of calculations and write down your times.

- Give your answers as whole numbers and common fractions. These are called 'mixed numbers'.

Set A

1 173 ÷ 7 =

2 269 ÷ 4 =

3 823 ÷ 5 =

4 904 ÷ 6 =

5 750 ÷ 9 =

Now try these:

Set B

1 523 ÷ 3 =

2 338 ÷ 8 =

3 436 ÷ 7 =

4 197 ÷ 4 =

5 217 ÷ 6 =

Dear Helper,

This activity is to help your child calculate divisions by a single number, giving the answer as a whole number with any remainder expressed as a fraction. Please help your child by timing each set accurately.

Name:

Problems

You will need: a pencil and some more paper for your workings.

- Try to solve each of these problems.

- Write your answers in the spaces on this page.

- Bring all your papers back into school.

Memo

Four of us want to go to see 'Holiday on Ice' in Birmingham. The show is running from January 7th to the 21st inclusive. We would like to go on either the 15th or 19th. Bob has said that he is willing to drive us the 28 miles each way on the 15th, but he cannot make the 19th. His car's petrol consumption is approximately 35 m.p.g (miles per gallon). We will give him the cost of 2 gallons of petrol at £3.55 a gallon. If we go on 19th, then the coach fare will be £3.75 each.

When we tried to book our theatre seats we found that the theatre only had a box for six people available on the 15th, at a cost of £75.50, and seats priced at £15.00 on the 19th.

---

1 Find the cost per person of going to the theatre on both the 15th and 19th January. When would you go?

I would go on _____

2 When Mrs. Jay split her class into groups of four, there were two children left over. When she split them into groups of five, there was one child left.

How many children were there in the class?

_____

3 ([   ] × 7) + 13 = 181

Find [   ] and write it in the space.

4 Dad is tiling the kitchen floor. Each tile is 25cm square and there are six tiles in each box. How many boxes will he need to buy?

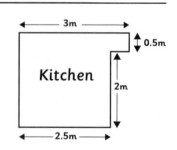

_____

5 Make up a story about: **a** 45 × 8   **b** 118 ÷ 3

Dear Helper,

Problems involving multiplication and division are featured here. It would be helpful if you could read the questions together before any work is undertaken. The answers can be written on this sheet, but encourage your child to save all their workings to take back to school.

Name:

Fractions everywhere

You will need: a pencil.

- Look at each of the statements below.
- Write the answers as common fractions in the boxes.

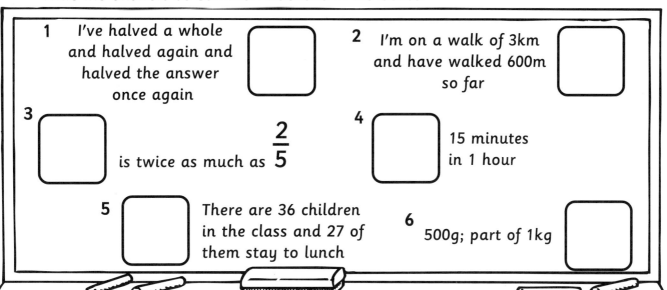

1 I've halved a whole and halved again and halved the answer once again

2 I'm on a walk of 3km and have walked 600m so far

3 is twice as much as $\frac{2}{5}$

4 15 minutes in 1 hour

5 There are 36 children in the class and 27 of them stay to lunch

6 500g; part of 1kg

7 Add together any of the answers above, to make 1 and record your sum.

8 Try to find another set of answers that make 1.

9 Can you make $\frac{3}{8}$, then $\frac{7}{8}$, by adding some of your answers? How?

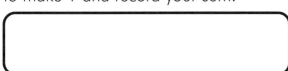

a $\frac{3}{8}$

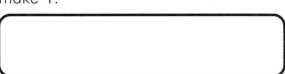

b $\frac{7}{8}$

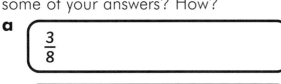

10 What about $\frac{7}{10}$?

- Can you find a way of adding all of them together? Show how.

Dear Helper,

This puzzle explores some aspects of fractions. Make sure that your child finds an answer for each box before they tackle the questions underneath. 'Equivalent' fractions will be needed in order to find some answers. For example, ⅜ is equivalent to ⅓ and ⁹⁄₂₇.

Broadacres Primary

You will need: a pencil and some paper.

A survey has been made of the 180 children who attend Broadacres Primary school.

Here are the results:

	The child…	Number of children	Fraction of the total number of children in the school
1	is a boy		$\frac{4}{9}$
2	has a dog	45	
3	has a cat	60	
4	has a pet which is neither a dog nor a cat	15	
5	has soccer as their favourite sport		$\frac{3}{5}$
6	visits the local swimming baths at least once a week		$\frac{1}{10}$
7	eats lunch at school regularly	140	
8	is a member of the school choir	36	

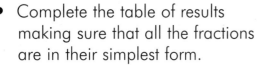

- Complete the table of results making sure that all the fractions are in their simplest form.

- Write down as much information as you can find from the table on paper to take back to school.

Here are some questions to start you off.

9 How many girls attend the school? _____

10 What fraction of children do not have a pet? _____

Dear Helper,	Continue on the back of this sheet or on some more paper.

This activity is to help your child use and apply fractions in statistical situations. It is an investigation, which means that your child must invent their own questions, find the answers to those questions and present their work in a clear form. When your child has finished, talk to them about their ideas.

Name:

Danehurst Road

You will need: a pencil and some paper.

There are 36 houses in Danehurst Road.
The houses are in the ratio of:
3 detached to 2 semi-detached to 1 bungalow.

1 How many houses in Danehurst Road are detached, how many are semi-detached and how many are bungalows?

_____

_____

2 There are 4 girls to every 3 boys living in the road and 16 girls live there. How many children live there?

_____

3 In the road, one of the semi-detached houses is painted white to every three which are not painted white. How many semi-detached houses are not painted white?

_____

4 What proportion of the semi-detached houses are:

a painted white? _____

b not painted white? _____

5 Invent other ratios, proportions and questions involving the houses and people who live in Danehurst Road and bring them to school.

Dear Helper,

The questions on this sheet follow up the work on ratio and proportions your child has done at school. Make sure that they have answered question 1 correctly, as 3 and 4 depend upon this. You may want to help with question 5. Suggest, for example, houses with garages, double glazing, occupants working in the local factory, but only do so if you are needed.

Name:

Karen and Rachael's money

You will need: a pencil and some paper, one piece for working out your answers and another for your decisions in question 6.

Karen and Rachael are twins. They each get £2.50 spending money a week.

1 Karen saves £0.75 and spends the rest.
What proportion of her spending money does she:

   a save?

   b spend?

   c What is her ratio of 'save' to 'spend'?

2 Rachael arranges her pocket money in a little more detail.

	Saving		**Spending**	
	Holiday, CDs and presents	Books	Sweets and chocolates	Other
Amount of money	£1.00	£0.25	£0.50	£0.75
Ratio				

• Fill in the ratio row in the table.

3 What proportion of her money does Rachael save?

4 What fraction of Rachael's money goes on sweets and chocolates?

5 In one year how much more money does Rachael save than Karen?

6 If you had £2.50 each week, how would you arrange to save or spend it? Write down your decisions on a separate piece of paper and bring it to school.

Dear Helper,

This activity applies ideas of ratio and proportion to money. It also encourages some thought about money management.

Name:

Over, under and between

You will need: a pencil.

1 Write these numbers in ascending order:

| 7.2 | 7.18 | 7.04 | 7.9 | 7.32 | 7.88 | 6.99 | 8 |

_____

2 Write these numbers in descending order:

| 0.42 | 0.38 | 0.56 | 0.6 | 0.7 | 0.47 | 0.39 | 0.65 |

_____

3 Write down some decimals which are:

a between 0.8 and 1.1 _____

b no less than 17.6, and
no more than 19.6 _____

c between 0.4 and 0.5 _____

d 0.5 away from 5.2 _____

e 0.25 more than 3.85 _____

4 a What is the smallest number you can
think of, that is greater than 3.5? _____

b What is the highest number below
50 you can think of? _____

5 What is the common fraction value of the underlined digit:

a 30.6̲3 _____   **d** 28.79̲8 _____

b 1̲75.8 _____   **e** 8.364̲ _____

c 18.32̲ _____   **f** 27.0̲21 _____

Dear Helper,

At school your child has been working with decimal numbers. Please look over the answers and discuss
any problems, but let your child tackle the sheet first.

PHOTOCOPIABLE

41

Stop the clock fractions

You will need: a pencil, a calculator, a watch with a seconds hand and a helper to time you.

- Convert the following common fractions to decimal fractions.

- Ask your Helper to time you.

- Try each set and write down your times.

- Only use the calculator when you need to, as this will slow you down.

Set 1

a $\frac{1}{10}$ **d** $\frac{1}{8}$

b $\frac{2}{100}$ **e** $\frac{1}{5}$

c $\frac{1}{2}$ **f** $\frac{2}{3}$

- Write down the difference between the following fractions as a decimal:

g $\frac{1}{8}$ and $\frac{1}{2}$ **h** $\frac{4}{5}$ and $\frac{5}{8}$

- Convert the following common fractions to decimal fractions.

Set 2

a $\frac{3}{100}$ **d** $\frac{1}{3}$

b $\frac{5}{1000}$ **e** $\frac{3}{8}$

c $\frac{1}{4}$ **f** $\frac{1}{9}$

Write as a decimal the sum of:

g $\frac{1}{3}$ and $\frac{1}{4}$ **h** $\frac{1}{100}$ and $\frac{2}{5}$

Set 3

a $7\frac{3}{4}$ **d** $6\frac{2}{3}$

b $2\frac{7}{10}$ **e** $4\frac{1}{8}$

c $8\frac{2}{5}$ **f** $9\frac{7}{8}$

Write as a decimal the sum of:

g $\frac{1}{9}$ and $\frac{1}{3}$ **h** $\frac{6}{1000}$ and $5\frac{3}{4}$

Dear Helper,

These sets of activities will help your child to become confident when changing common fractions to decimal fractions. Please help your child by timing each set accurately.

Name:

One to fifty

You will need: a pencil and some scrap paper.

- Use the numbers 1 to 50 and fill in the table below. A few have been done for you.

- Choose two other multiples to investigate. Record your answers in the blank columns.

Numbers 1 to 50						
	Odd numbers	Multiples of 2	Multiples of 4	Multiples of 7		
How many?	25		12			
Proportion of the numbers tested				$\frac{7}{50}$		
Percentage of the numbers tested		50%				

- What percentage are:

  a not multiples of 5?

  b multiples of both 5 and 7?

  c multiples of both 4 and 8?

Challenge!

- Make up some more questions like those above and find the answers. This time use the numbers 1 to 100.

Dear Helper,

The questions on the sheet use your child's knowledge of multiples, linking this to proportion and percentage ideas. The challenge is for more able children who complete questions 1 to 3 quickly and confidently. Work with your child if you feel you can help!

Name:

Paris

You will need: a pencil, some paper and a calculator.

Dad and Mum are off to Paris. A copy of the information given to them by their travel agent is shown below:

a for the period 28th December – 4th January,

b for the period 27th January – 31st March.

- Investigate the various hotel costs of a long weekend for two people, Friday to Tuesday (four nights), in Paris during March.

Hotel	Cost per night, per person	Transport to Paris	Special offers etc	Meal arrangements
Splendide **a** **b**	 161 99	 Air Air		Accommodation, breakfast
Vibrant **a** **b**	 169 141	 Eurostar Eurostar	One night free in stays of 3 nights or more	Accommodation
Eiffel **a** **b**	 184 156	 Air Air	One free dinner for stays of 3 nights or more	Accommodation, breakfast
Triomphe **a** **b**	 205 189	 Air Eurostar	One night free in stays of 3 nights or more for Sunday arrivals	Accommodation, breakfast, dinner
Gaete **a** **b**	 265 246	Air or Eurostar	Guests staying 3 nights or more receive a complimentary gift	Accommodation, breakfast

Which hotel do you think Dad and Mum should choose and why?

_____

_____

Dear Helper,

In class your child has been extracting and interpreting data using holidays as a theme. Encourage your child to consider all the various possibilities before deciding on a 'best buy' and justifying their choice. Your child may use a calculator if it helps.

Name:

Touring Paris

You will need: a pencil, writing paper and rough paper.

Take **'Les Cars Blue'** and discover the main sites of Paris in a relaxed way.

*Nine 'Les Cars Blue' stops are scheduled and you may
break your tour at any 'Les Cars Blue' stop and continue later.*

STOPS	Tour A	Tour B	Tour C	Tour 1	Tour 2	Tour 3	Tour 4	Tour 5	Tour 6	Tour 7	Tour 8
TROCADÉRO				09.20	09.45	10.10	10.35	11.00	11.25	11.50	12.15
TOUR EIFFEL				09.45	10.10	10.35	11.00	11.25	11.50	12.15	12.40
CHAMP DE MARS				09.50	10.15	10.40	11.05	11.30	11.55	12.20	12.45
MUSÉE DU LOUVRE				10.10	10.35	11.00	11.25	11.50	12.15	12.40	13.05
NOTRE-DAME			10.00	10.25	10.50	11.15	11.40	12.05	12.30	12.55	13.20
MUSÉE D'ORSAY			10.15	10.40	11.05	11.30	11.55	12.20	12.45	13.10	13.35
OPÉRA/GALERIES LAFAYETTE		10.05	10.30	10.55	11.20	11.45	12.10	12.35	13.00	13.25	13.50
CHAMPS ELYSÉES	10.10	10.35	11.00	11.25	11.50	12.15	12.40	13.05	13.30	13.55	14.20
GRAND PALAIS	10.20	10.45	11.10	11.35	12.00	12.25	12.50	13.15	13.40	14.05	14.30
TROCADÉRO	10.35	11.00	11.25	11.50	12.15	12.40	13.05	13.30	13.55	14.20	14.45

1   How long is a complete tour?

2   The tours run every 25 minutes and the last tour begins at the
Trocadéro at 16.25. How many tours have not been shown on
the timetable above?

3   Jay has arranged to meet Paul at the Opera/Lafayette at 13.15,
she is at the Trocadéro. Which tour bus must she catch?

4   Paul leaves the Tour 2 bus at Notre-Dame and spends 55 minutes
sightseeing, and returning to the bus stop. Which tour bus will he
now catch?

5   Imran took the Tour C bus from Notre-Dame to Musée D'Orsay
where he spent 2 hours 20 minutes. He decided to walk from the
Musée to Grand Palais, taking 12 minutes. At the Grand Palais he
caught the first available bus back to his hotel near Champ de
Mars. What time did he arrive at the Champ de Mars?

6   Make up two questions about 'Les Cars Blue' timetable to ask a friend.
You will need to work out the answers first, to check your friend's work.

Dear Helper,

Paris is the setting for this homework and this unusual bus timetable provides the data. Before your child
begins the exercise, encourage them to read the timetable. Your child may need help understanding how
'Les Cars Blue' operate. All working out should be done on rough paper and should accompany this
homework back to school.

Name:

Fun Run

You will need: a pencil, ruler, graph paper and a calculator.

Cotleigh Village Council organised a Fun Run around the village to raise funds for a new hall. Each runner under 16 paid 50p to enter the Fun Run, while those aged 16 and over paid £1.00.

The chart below shows the number of runners of each age.

Age	Number of runners	Age	Number of runners	Age	Number of runners
7	1	19	8	29	5
9	3	21	12	30	6
10	4	22	16	32	4
11	1	23	19	33	3
12	14	24	14	34	4
13	11	25	10	35	2
14	17	26	8	37	2
15	9	27	5	43	1
17	10	28	2	49	1

- Draw a graph to show this information.

- How many runners were there?

_____

- How much money was raised?

_____

Dear Helper,

Your child will first need to group the data into suitable age ranges before drawing the graph. Five or ten year ranges would be suitable, for example 6 - 10 year olds, 11 - 15 year olds and so on. Calculators may be used to help provide answers to the questions.

Name:

What are the chances?

You will need: a set of playing cards, a pencil and some paper.

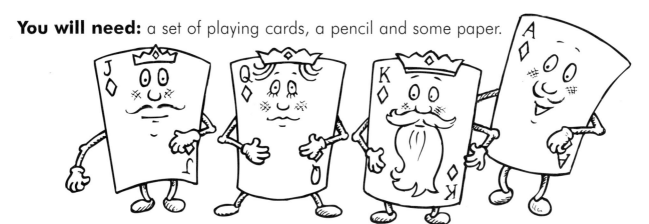

- Use only the Jack, Queen, King and Ace of diamonds from the pack of cards. Shuffle the cards and lay them picture side down.

1 What are the chances of turning over the King? Why?

- Now add the Jack, Queen, King and Ace of Hearts to the set of diamond picture cards and shuffle them. Spread them out on the table, face down.

2 What are the chances of turning over:

a a Jack?

b the Queen of Hearts?

c What are the chances of the card not being a Diamond?

- Now add the Jack, Queen, King and Ace of Spades to your set. Shuffle the cards and place them face down.

3 If you turn over one card, what are the chances of it being:

a a Spade?

b the Ace of Diamonds?

c a Queen?

- Using just the Jack, Queen, King and Ace of Spades, have **20** turns at shuffling the cards, laying them face down and choosing one.

4 Record what cards you turn over on a separate sheet of paper. Replace the card you chose each time.

a What can you say about these results?

b Are they what you expected?

Dear Helper,

At school your child has been investigating the chance of a coin showing 'heads' when tossed. This activity extends the idea from two possibilities to four, eight and twelve. You might like to talk to your child about their results and the reasoning behind them.

PHOTOCOPIABLE

Name:

Know your cars

SEAT

MERCEDES

PEUGEOT

CITROËN

VAUXHALL

RENAULT

PORSCHE

ROVER

HONDA

TOYOTA

You will need: a pencil, scissors and some paper.

- Cut out the badges shown above and fold back the names of the cars so that they cannot be seen.

  How good are people at recognising car badges?

- Using the ten car badges above, test at least 10 of your family and friends as a sample.

- Make a table of results on the back of this sheet.

- What do your results show?

  Do the results help you to make any predictions about:

  a How good children are at recognising car badges?

  _____

  b Whether adults are better than children?

  _____

- Can you say anything else about your results?

  _____

Dear Helper,

Your child has been using sampling ideas to test skill and to see how the sample may be used to give an indication of what the results might be if a larger set of people were tested. Encourage your child to talk about the validity of sampling and make other predictions based on the results.

Name:

Estimating angles

You will need: a pencil, a protractor and a watch
or clock to time five minutes.

- Estimate these angles but do not measure them.

- Write each estimate in the column on the table below.

- You have five minutes. Ask your helper to tell you when your
  time is up.

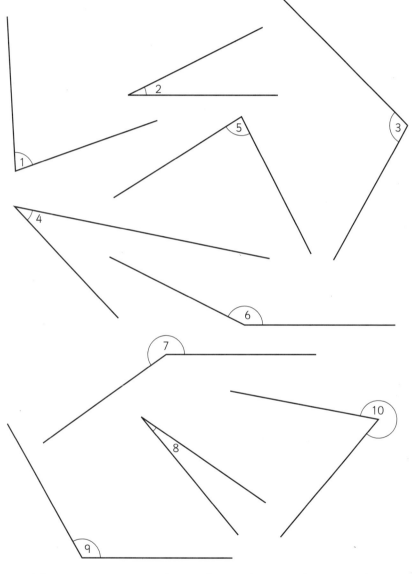

	Estimate	Measurement
1		
2		
3		
4		
5		
6		
7		
8		
9		
10		

- Now measure each angle and write these in the measurement
  column. Do not change your estimate!

Dear Helper,

It is important that your child can estimate the size of an angle before going on to measure it accurately
using a protractor. That way they will know if the measurement is about right. They are encouraged to do
this in many measurement and calculation activities at school. This activity is designed to give your child
experience and confidence in the estimation of angles and in the use of a protractor to measure them.
Please allow your child just five minutes to do the estimation.

Name:

Measure and calculate

You will need: a pencil and a protractor.

- Use your protractor to measure each of the angles marked with a dot.

- Write its value on the triangle.

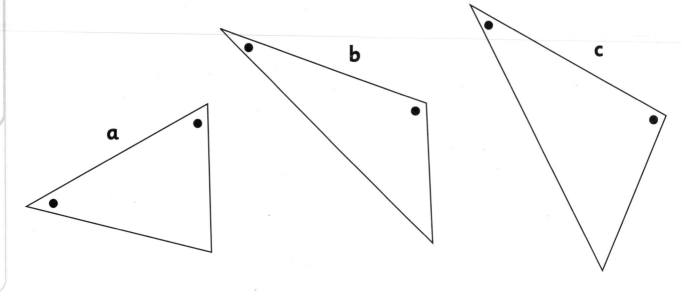

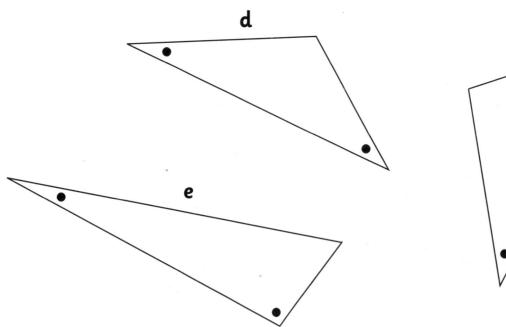

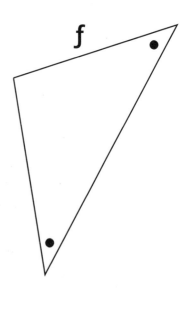

- Now put your protractor away and calculate the value of the other angles.

- Write these on the appropriate triangles.

Dear Helper,

Your child has been measuring angles and calculating the number of degrees in the angles of a triangle. This activity gives them the opportunity to measure two of the angles, and to calculate the third angle of each triangle.

Making triangles

You will need: a few drinking straws, scissors and a pencil.

- Cut your drinking straws into the following lengths:
  three lengths of 4cm,
  three lengths of 6cm,
  three lengths of 8cm,
  three lengths of 10cm.

  Using any of the 12 pieces of straw, how many different types of triangles can you make?

- Record your results on the table below.
  One has been done for you.

Lengths of straws used (in cm)	Type of triangle					
	equilateral	isosceles	right angled	scalene	obtuse angled	acute angled
4, 4, 4	✓					✓

What do you notice?

Dear Helper,

This investigation is a follow-up to the work your child has begun in class on identifying and naming different types of triangle. Encourage your child to break down the problem, perhaps by keeping two straw lengths constant and varying the length of the third. Not all combinations of straw lengths will make a triangle. Your child may make the same type of triangle using different straws. Although these can be recorded, they should not be counted as different types of triangle.

Name:

I'm thinking of...

You will need: scissors, a pencil, some paper and a helper.

- Select one of the shapes and write its name on your paper, but do not tell your partner what it is.

- Now give your partner a clue to the shape by telling them an attribute of the shape.

  For example, if you have selected a trapezium you may say: I am thinking of a shape with some parallel sides.

- Your partner should now try to name the shape. If they are unsuccessful, give another clue.

- Continue until your partner names the shape correctly. They should do this in five clues or less.

- Record the number of clues they needed on a score sheet.

  Each person has four turns. The winner is the player who needed the least clues.

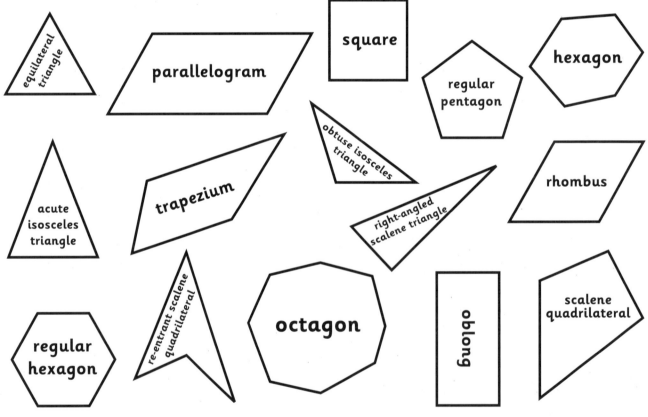

Dear Helper,

The class have spent the last two lessons looking at the attributes – special features – of triangles (all shapes with three straight sides) and quadrilaterals (all shapes with four straight sides). This game uses the knowledge they have gained and also draws in other polygons. As well as positive attributes, negative attributes are also valid. For example, the parallelogram shown <u>does not have</u> four equal sides.

Name:

Cubes again

You will need: a ruler, protractor, pencil, and some rough paper.

- Think of a cube-shaped box without a lid.

- On this sheet sketch as many nets of this box as you can.

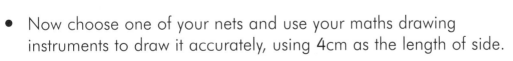

- Now choose one of your nets and use your maths drawing instruments to draw it accurately, using 4cm as the length of side.

- Cut it out and see if it does make a box without a lid.

- Bring it back to school.

Dear Helper,

Your child may need help to visualise the net of the cube (the flat shape that folds up to make a cube) and they should be encouraged to sketch and then cut out their ideas on rough paper before attempting to record their ideas on the sheet.

Name: _____

Perimeters and formulae

You will need: a pencil.

1   Write in words how to find the perimeter of a rhombus using the length of one side.

It starts: Measure the length... _____

_____

• Write the formula using letters. Don't forget to say what the letters represent.

_____

2   The table shows the length of side and perimeters of some regular shapes.

Length of side l	Perimeter p
2cm	14cm
15cm	105cm
5mm	35mm
17m	119m

• What kind of shapes have been measured? How do you know?

_____

• Which formula, using letters, could relate the lengths of side (l) with the perimeters (p)?

_____

3   Using letters write down the formula for finding the perimeter of crosses, shaped like this, if the length l is known.

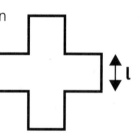

4   Create a formula for finding the perimeter of this shape using lengths **a** and **b**.

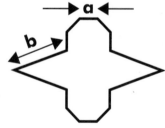

• What is the perimeter of a cross whose length l is 6cm?

_____

• Measure the lengths **a** and **b** and use your formula to find the perimeter.

_____

Dear Helper,

At school your child has been learning about formulae. For example, for a square: p = 4l. If they find difficulty with the first question, carefully draw a rhombus like this ⟋⟋ on a separate piece of paper and discuss the fact that each side is the same length.

Name:

Measurements everywhere

You will need: a pencil, some paper and a clipboard.

- Investigate units of metric measurement used in the 'real world': in the kitchen, in the supermarket, at a garage, at the chemist, at a DIY superstore and so on.

- Ask your Helper to work with you and jot down all you discover. Search for as many different units as you can.

- Write a report and classify your findings under Length, Mass (Weight), Capacity and Area.

  Your findings will help build up the class lists.

PHOTOCOPIABLE

Dear Helper,

This activity is to share with your child. Make a suitable clipboard and set out on the investigation. Let your child write the report and produce the lists for taking back to school.

SOLVING PROBLEMS

MAKING DECISIONS

Name:

Find the partner

You will need: a pencil and some paper.

- Find the subtraction partner for each addition.

- Work out the answers mentally. Use jottings to check each result with an equivalent calculation.

- Write down the strategies you used to find each answer on a separate piece of paper and bring it to school. One of the pairs has been found for you.

Additions

1   8.9 + 3.1 =   12

2   1.4 + 15.8 =

3   453 + 217 =

4   6.2 + 8.8 =

5   283 + 487 =

6   138.5 + 22.5 =

7   7.7 + 3.3 =

8   16.6 + 16.4 =

Subtractions

a   915 − 245 =

b   154.1 − 143.1 =

c   499 − 338 =

d   29.8 − 12.6 =

e   1 028 − 1 016 =   12

f   1 115 − 345 =

g   100 − 67 =

h   87 − 72 =

Question 1 pairs with e.
For 8.9 + 3.1, I thought it's like
9 + 3 = 12. To check, I used 8.9 + 3 = 11.9
and another 0.1 makes 12. For 1028 − 1016,
I said it's like 1030 − 1018 = 12 and
checked by saying it's really only
16 + [ ] = 28 giving 12.

9   Which pair's answer is:

i) a half of 1540?

ii) 8.6 doubled?

PHOTOCOPIABLE

Dear Helper,

Mental agility is most important. 'Find the partner' not only practises this but also asks for each strategy used to be explained. Why not try some yourself? Hide the calculator!

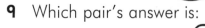

Name:

Walk the tightrope

You will need: your helper as a partner to play against.
Two suits from a pack of playing cards (say clubs and diamonds), cards 1 to 9 only, two counters or 5p coins, two pencils, two pieces of paper and a calculator.

- Place counters for you and your partner at the START positions on the board below. Ask your helper to shuffle the clubs and diamonds cards separately.

- Take a club for your tens digit, and then a diamond for your units digit.

- Tell your partner the 'pair number to 100' and write it down on your paper. For example, if your cards showed 68 you would say and write down 32, because 68 add 32 makes 100.

- Check with the calculator. If you are wrong your turn ends. If you are correct, draw another club and diamond and mentally add the number formed to the number you wrote down.

- Tell your partner your answer and check with a calculator. If you are wrong, your counter stays where it is. If you are right, move your counter one place along the tightrope.

- Now it is your partner's turn.

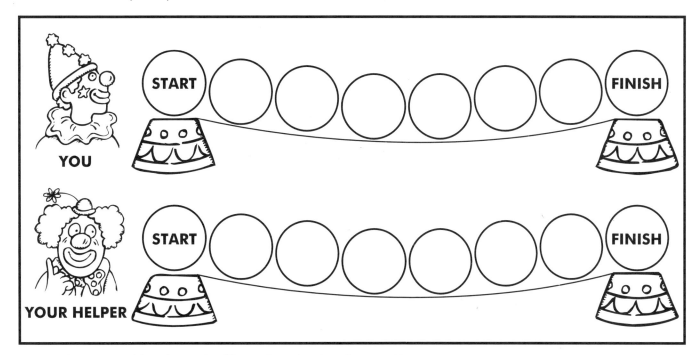

- Continue like this, shuffling the cards after each turn.

    The winner is the first player to reach the FINISH.

Dear Helper,

'Walk the tightrope' will help your child, and you perhaps, to know 'pair numbers to 100,' that is, to know the difference between a number and 100. It also helps with adding two, two-digit numbers. Enjoy yourselves!

Name:

Decicalc additions

You will need: a pencil.

DO NOT USE A CALCULATOR

- Estimate the answers to these additions.
- Write your estimates in the table below. The first one has been done for you.

1 16.3 + 179.82   **2** 0.94 + 7.35   **3** 1 057.8 + 198.3

4 29.6 + 13.8 + 0.9   **5** 48.71 + 21.36 + 18.7

Question Number	1	2	3	4	5
Estimate	196				

- Record each estimation strategy. The first question has been done.

1 I rounded down 16.3 to 16 and rounded up 179.82 to 180, so my estimation is 196.

2 _____

_____

3 _____

_____

4 _____

_____

5 _____

_____

- Calculate the answers using vertical columns.

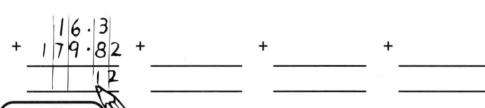

```
   1 6 . 3
+ 1 7 9 . 8 2      +              +              +
_____      ___            ___            ___
         1 2
```

Dear Helper,

These decimal additions encourage good estimation and accurate calculation. Talk to your child about their estimation strategies. Hide the calculator!

Decicalc subtractions

You will need: a pencil.

DO NOT USE A CALCULATOR

- Estimate the answers to these subtractions.

   1 17.9 – 6.18   **2** 103.1 – 77.07   **3** 36.41 – 32.8

   4 253 – 19.63   **5** 1 040 – 782.4

Question Number	1	2	3	4	5
Estimate					

- Calculate the answers using vertical subtractions.

6 In Simpsons a jacket cost £35.61, but in Tuckers it cost £39.18. What is the difference in price?

7 Simeon's family has a Rover car which has a mileage reading of 1 738.4. Daljit's family's new Ford car reads 36.8. How many more miles has the Rover travelled than the Ford?

Dear Helper,

Decimal subtraction calculations are featured on this sheet. Estimation, accurate calculation and 'real life' application are practised. Your methods of calculation may be different to those taught at school. Let your child use the method they have been taught, otherwise confusion can arise. Hide the calculator! Talk with your child about other decimal subtraction situations which involve measure, for example, weight, capacity, times for athletic events.

Name:

Square number challenge

You will need: a pencil, a watch or clock and a helper to time you.

1	4	9	16	25	36	49	64	81	100	121	144
1^2	2^2	3^2	4^2	5^2	6^2	7^2	8^2	9^2	10^2	11^2	12^2

- See how many different ways you can make the target number by using square numbers up to 12×12. You may add, subtract, multiply or divide.

- Allow five minutes for each number.

- Ask your helper to check the time.

The first question has been done for you.

1 9
3^2 (that's easy)
$2^2 + 2^2 + 1^2$
$5^2 - 4^2$
$(2^2 - 1^2) \times (2^2 - 1^2)$
$9^2 \div 3^2$

2 5

3 36

4 3^2

5 45

6 144

Your Helper might like to try each target number so that you can compare your results, or you may choose to work together.

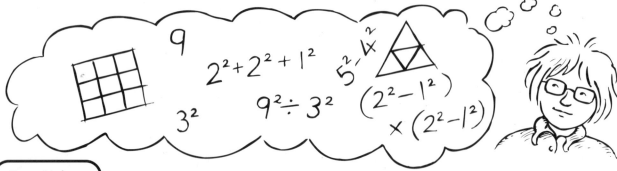

Dear Helper,

At school your child has been building square numbers and developing the sequence 1, 4, 9, 16, 25 and so on. Join in the challenge if you would like to. Be sure to restrict the time allowed for each question to five minutes.

100 MATHS HOMEWORK ACTIVITIES • YEAR 6 TERM 1

Name:

Sequences and term numbers

You will need: a pencil, some paper and a calculator.

1 Here is the start of the square number sequence together with term numbers.

- Continue the pattern to the 7th term.

Term number n	Square number n^2
1	1
2	4
3	9
4	16
5	
6	
7	

- Find the square numbers for:

a the 11th term _____

b the 13th term _____

c the 40th term _____

d the 100th term _____

2 Use $n^2 + 9$ for the sequence which starts:

Term number n	$n^2 + 9$
1	10
2	13
3	18
4	
5	
6	
7	

3 Find the first five terms for:

a

Term number n	$n^2 - 5$
1	
2	
3	
4	
5	

b

Term number n	$n^2 \times 4$
1	
2	
3	
4	
5	

c

Term number n	$n^2 \div 2$
1	
2	
3	
4	
5	

4 Investigate how each of these sequences is related to square numbers. Question **a** has been answered for you.

a

Term number n	$n^2 \times 5$
1	5
2	20
3	45
4	80
5	125
100	50 000

b

Term number n	
1	14
2	17
3	22
4	29
5	38
100	10 013

c

Term number n	
1	0.25
2	1
3	2.25
4	4
5	6.25
100	2 500

- Try other sequences and their term numbers. Write up your findings on a separate sheet and bring it to school.

Dear Helper,

This sheet follows up the work on sequences and term numbers which your child has been studying at school. If they find difficulty with a question, it is important to talk it through with them. For example, for the first term in question 2, say: '1 × 1 is 1, add 9 is 10'; for the second term say: '2 × 2 is 4, add 9 is 13', and so on.

Name:

Pascal's triangle

You will need: a pencil and some paper.

A mathematician named Pascal laid out numbers in the triangular arrangement shown. It is called an array.

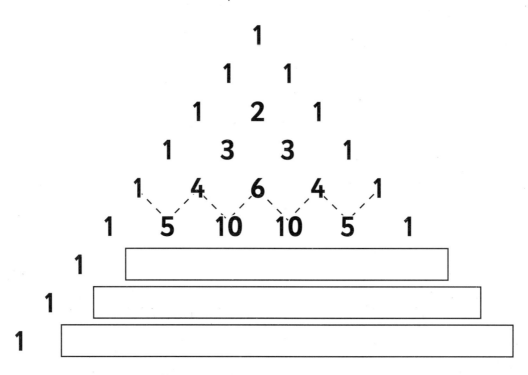

- Can you extend it another three rows? Be careful where you place each number.

- Investigate the numbers in the array and write down everything you find out on a separate sheet of paper.

    Here are some clues:

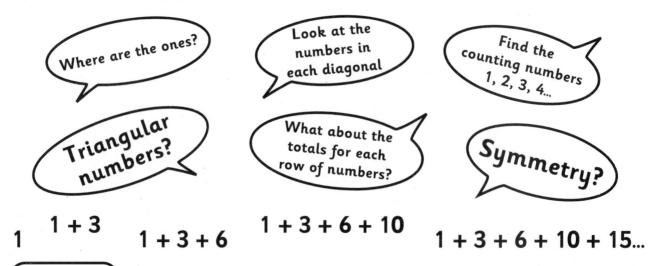

Where are the ones?

Look at the numbers in each diagonal

Find the counting numbers 1, 2, 3, 4…

Triangular numbers?

What about the totals for each row of numbers?

Symmetry?

1   1 + 3   1 + 3 + 6   1 + 3 + 6 + 10   1 + 3 + 6 + 10 + 15…

Dear Helper,

Following the work in school on square numbers such as 1, 4, 9, 16, and triangular numbers such as 1, 3, 6, 10, this activity sets your child on a voyage of discovery which gives glimpses of the wonderful patterns which mathematics can give. Perhaps you would like to 'sail' with them.

Name:

About how many?

You will need: a pencil, some paper and a calculator.

- Work out the answers to the following questions on paper, laying out your steps clearly. Record the answers below.

- Take your paper to school when you have completed the homework.

1 a How many hours have you been alive? Be as accurate as you can.

_____

b Work out how many hours other members of your family have been alive.

_____

c What is the total number of hours lived by the children in your class? This will be an approximate answer, so round it to make it reasonable.

_____

2 a About how many days have there been since the birth of Jesus?

_____

b How many hours is this?

_____

c Discuss with your Helper how many years there are in a generation. Now work out how many generations there have been since Jesus was born.

_____

3 The heart beats about **70** times per minute when a person is resting. At this rate, about how many times does it beat in:

a a day _____

b a year _____

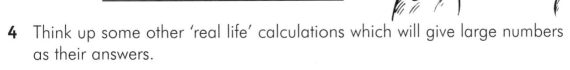

4 Think up some other 'real life' calculations which will give large numbers as their answers.

Dear Helper,

Talk with your child about the questions on this sheet, for example, how many years would be reasonable for a generation? Remember, a generation is not a lifetime! Ask: By what age would most people have produced the next generation? Encourage them to produce interesting ideas for question 4 and remind them to write their strategies clearly.

Name:

Goals!

You will need: A pencil, rough paper and a newspaper that includes Football League tables.

Work with your Helper if you need to.

1 At the end of the 1986/87 football season the bottom of the 4th Division looked like this:

	Points	Goals for (F)	Goals against (A)	Goal difference
Torquay United	48	56	72	−16
Lincoln City	48	45	65	−20

Can you explain why Torquay United were placed above Lincoln City?

_____

_____

2 In the previous season, 1985/86, four teams ended with 54 points. Can you place them in their correct league positions based on goal difference?

The highest team was 19th and the lowest 22nd.

League position	Points	Goals for (F)	Goals against (A)	Goal difference
19				
20				
21				
22				

3 Look at the present league tables in a newspaper and record some of the teams whose goal difference gives a negative number result. That is, teams which have had more goals scored against them, than they have scored themselves.

Dear Helper,

At school your child has been exploring positive and negative numbers and applying them in various situations. Share this homework with them if they need assistance. If you need help with reading the league tables, ask someone at home or 'phone a friend!'

Find the clues

You will need: a pencil and some rough paper.

Here is a cross-number puzzle, unfortunately all the clues have become muddled.

- Sort the clues and place them in their correct positions.
- Use the rough paper to work out the multiplications.

Grid:
1	3	6	8	
	7	0	7	4
1	6	3	5	
8	5			
2	9	4	6	4

Clues: 26 × 7   545 × 3   3 683 × 8   342 × 4   175 × 5   786 × 9   851 × 9

Clues across	**Clues down**
1 _____	2 _____
3 _____	3 _____
4 _____	4 _____
5 _____	

- Take your rough paper to school when the work is complete.

Dear Helper,

This homework practises the written multiplication of larger numbers by a single digit. It will be necessary for your child to use the rough paper to work out the answers to the clues before writing them on the sheet. Hide the calculator!

Name:

First to the top

You will need: a helper to play against, pencils, a calculator and one set of function cards: ×2, ×3, ×4, ×5, ×6, ×7, ×8, ×9.

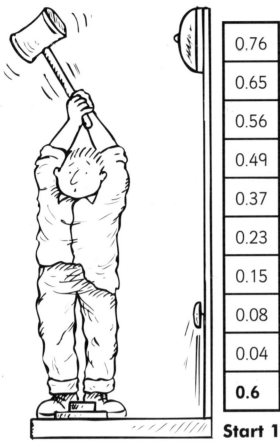

Start 1
0.76
0.65
0.56
0.49
0.37
0.23
0.15
0.08
0.04
0.6

Start 2
0.75
0.63
0.47
0.59
0.28
0.32
0.14
0.06
0.05
0.7

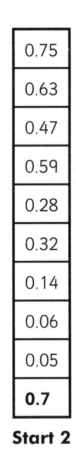
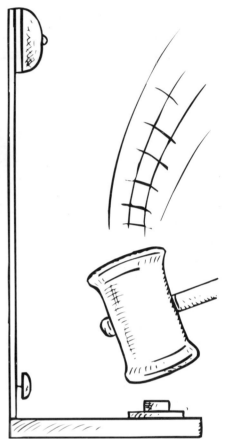

- Shuffle the function cards and place them in a pile face down.

- Turn over the top function card and multiply 0.6 by the function on the card.

- Let your partner check your answer with a calculator. If your partner agrees with your answer, cross off 0.6. If you are not correct then do not cross off 0.6.

- Place the function card at the bottom of the pile.

- Now it is your partner's turn to take a card and multiply 0.7 by the function shown on it.

Play continues in this way with the winner being the first player to the top.

Dear Helper,

This game is intended to give your child practice in mentally multiplying a decimal by a whole number. Quick recall of multiplication facts will be necessary and your child may need help with place value.

Name:

Decorating

You will need: a pencil and some rough paper.

DO NOT USE A CALCULATOR

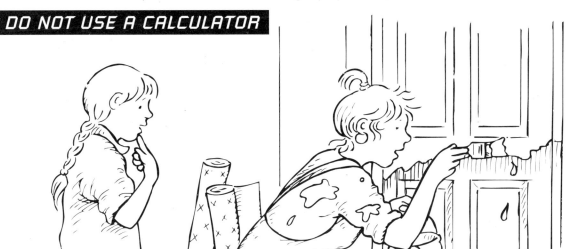

My Mum has saved £200 to re-decorate my bedroom. I have been choosing the materials that I want. Here is my list:

3 tins of paint (2 emulsion, 1 gloss) @ £6.75 each cost

5 rolls of textured wallpaper @ £3.64 per roll cost

9 square metres of carpet @ £9.23 per square metre cost

6 metres of curtain fabric @ £5.86 per metre cost

What is the total cost of the materials and how much money will not be spent?

_____

I hope to decorate my walls with three posters costing £4.99 each.
Have we got enough to do this?

_____

If so, how much will be left for Mum after we have finished my bedroom?

_____

Dear Helper,

In class your child has been using informal pencil and paper methods to solve multiplication calculations, and this activity gives additional practice. Encourage them to show all their working on the rough paper, which should accompany this sheet back to school. Calculators are not allowed!

Name:

Multiplications

You will need: a pencil, some paper, a watch with a seconds hand and a helper to time you.

- Work out the answers to these multiplication calculations. Show all your working on this sheet.

- Ask your Helper to time you, one set at a time.

DO NOT USE A CALCULATOR

Set 1

1 $3.62 \times 4 =$	**2** $4.17 \times 6 =$
3 $6.58 \times 3 =$	**4** $8.09 \times 7 =$
5 $5.46 \times 9 =$	Time:

Set 2

1 $7.23 \times 5 =$	**2** $9.34 \times 8 =$
3 $3.75 \times 4 =$	**4** $4.82 \times 6 =$
5 $6.97 \times 3 =$	Time:

- Choose two of the multiplications and make up 'real life' contexts. You may need to use an extra sheet of paper for this.

Remember to bring all the paper you use with you to school.

Dear Helper,

These sets of activities give practice in the written method of multiplication and all working should be shown on the sheet. Please time each set accurately.

Name:

Find the function

You will need: a pencil, some rough paper and a calculator.

- Use one of these functions to complete each of the divisions shown below.

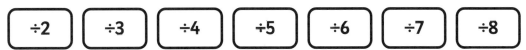

| ÷2 | ÷3 | ÷4 | ÷5 | ÷6 | ÷7 | ÷8 |

- Use rough paper for your working and do not use a calculator.

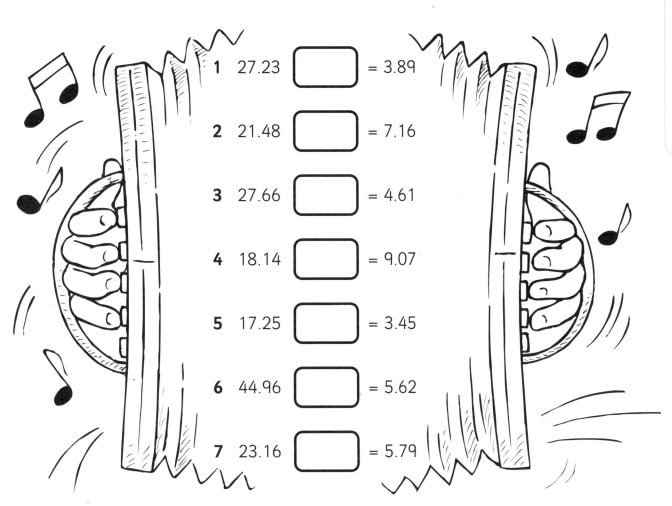

1 27.23 ☐ = 3.89

2 21.48 ☐ = 7.16

3 27.66 ☐ = 4.61

4 18.14 ☐ = 9.07

5 17.25 ☐ = 3.45

6 44.96 ☐ = 5.62

7 23.16 ☐ = 5.79

Now check your answers with a calculator.

Dear Helper,

In class your child has been solving decimal division calculations by first estimating the result and then going on to use informal written methods of multiplication. Ensure that your child shows all their working on rough paper before entering the answer on to the sheet. All rough working should accompany this homework when it is returned to school.

Name:

Decimal divisions

You will need: a pencil, paper to work on, a ruler and a helper to time you.

- Work out the answers to these decimal divisions on paper.

- Ask your Helper to time how long it takes you to complete each set.

DO NOT USE A CALCULATOR

When you have finished each set, write the answers on this homework sheet.

Set 1

1 $52.2 \div 3 =$ ⬚   **2** $81.5 \div 5 =$ ⬚

3 $258.3 \div 7 =$ ⬚   **4** $132.3 \div 9 =$ ⬚

5 $49.6 \div 2 =$ ⬚

Time taken: _____

Set 2

1 $218.8 \div 4 =$ ⬚   **2** $446.4 \div 6 =$ ⬚

3 $777.6 \div 8 =$ ⬚   **4** $81.9 \div 3 =$ ⬚

5 $144.5 \div 5 =$ ⬚

Time taken: _____

Choose any three of the divisions and make up 'real life' contexts.

_____

_____

_____

Dear Helper,

In class your child has extended written methods to short division of numbers involving decimals, and this homework provides practice. Each calculation and the answers should be shown on paper and the answers written on this sheet. Please time each set accurately.

Name:

Cash and Carry

You will need: a calculator and a pencil.

Here is Mum's shopping list for the Cash and Carry:

12 tins of Fido @ **37p** a tin

12 tins of Tibs @ **38p** a tin

6 bottles of cola @ **46p** a bottle

3 bottles of squash @ **78p** a bottle

6 packs of fruit juice @ **65p** a pack

6 tins of soup @ **27p** a tin

4 packs of soap @ **99p** a pack

- Use the Memory facility on your calculator to find the total cost of Mum's shopping.

- Record the keys you pressed.

- On the back of this sheet, make up a Cash and Carry shopping list for your friend to solve. Make sure you have worked out the answer before they start.

Dear Helper,

In class your child has been learning to use the Memory facility on the calculator. Encourage them to give a rough estimate before they begin to use the calculator and to remember how they used Memory for discussion in class. The recording of the keys pressed will form the basis for this discussion.

Tinscombe town survey

You will need: a pencil and rough paper.

DO NOT USE A CALCULATOR

Two thousand, four hundred adults in Tinscombe answered a questionnaire about their town. This meant that about one in fifteen of the population took part.

1 About how many people live in Tinscombe?

2 Here are some of the results. Each fraction given is approximate.

About how many people voted for each of the suggestions?

a $\frac{7}{10}$ thought that the central streets should be made into a pedestrian area.

b $\frac{2}{3}$ voted for the introduction of a 'park-and-ride' scheme.

c $\frac{7}{12}$ voted for the new shopping precinct plans.

d $\frac{3}{4}$ voted against the proposed one-way traffic system.

e $\frac{5}{6}$ voted for the building of a new leisure centre.

3 Write the data shown below as a fraction of the number of people who answered the questionnaire.

Each number has been rounded to the nearest 10.

a 800 voted for a new 'out of town' supermarket.

b 720 wanted a theatre built.

Dear Helper,

These examples give practice in identifying the links between common fractions and survey data which your child has been working on at school. Encourage them to use rough paper to record any necessary steps to the answer.

Round up or down?

You will need: a pencil and a calculator.

1 Round these decimal numbers to the nearest whole number and then to the nearest tenth:

a 6.42

b 17.86

c 99.74

d 28.08

e 0.37

2 Use a calculator for these division calculations, but write down the answer correct to the nearest whole number.

a 16 ÷ 5

b 21.77 ÷ 14

c 19.68 ÷ 8

d 301.5 ÷ 9

e 617 ÷ 5

3 Round these divisions to the nearest tenth. Use a calculator to help you.

a 58 ÷ 7

b 13 ÷ 3

c 1 ÷ 9

d 65 ÷ 17

e 13 489 ÷ 6

4 Mr Hennessey weighs **80kg** to the nearest **kg**. What could his highest and lowest weight be, recorded to one place of decimals?

highest   lowest

Dear Helper,

At school your child has been rounding decimals to the nearest whole number and to the nearest tenth. These exercises give practice in doing this.

Name:

Low to high and round about

You will need: a pencil, rough paper and a calculator for use in questions 3 and 4 only.

$$0 \quad \frac{1}{8} \quad \frac{1}{4} \quad \frac{3}{8} \quad \frac{1}{2} \quad \frac{3}{4} \quad 1$$

Where does $\frac{3}{16}$ go?

1 Look at the picture and fill in the blanks.

a $\frac{3}{16}$ is between [ ] and [ ]

b $\frac{1}{10}$ is between [ ] and [ ]

c $\frac{7}{16}$ is between [ ] and [ ]

d $\frac{5}{8}$ is between [ ] and [ ]

e $\frac{7}{10}$ is between [ ] and [ ]

2 Order these fractions by converting them to fractions with a common denominator.

a $\frac{2}{5} \quad \frac{5}{6} \quad \frac{1}{2} \quad \frac{1}{6} \quad \frac{1}{3}$ _____

_____

b $\frac{3}{5} \quad \frac{1}{2} \quad \frac{7}{20} \quad \frac{1}{4} \quad \frac{2}{5}$ _____

_____

3 Use a calculator to change each of these fractions to a decimal by division, and use this information to write the common fractions in order.

a $\frac{3}{8} \quad \frac{4}{15} \quad \frac{3}{5} \quad \frac{1}{3} \quad \frac{7}{12} \quad \frac{2}{3}$ _____

_____

b $\frac{5}{6} \quad \frac{7}{8} \quad \frac{6}{7} \quad \frac{4}{5} \quad \frac{9}{10} \quad \frac{13}{16}$ _____

_____

4 Write down one easy common fraction which you think is nearest to all the fractions shown. $\frac{3}{13} \quad \frac{4}{15} \quad \frac{1}{5} \quad \frac{3}{10} \quad \frac{2}{9} \quad \frac{5}{17}$ [ ]

Dear Helper,

This activity helps your child to order both common and decimal fractions and to relate the two systems used for expressing fractional parts. Let them use rough paper for calculations and only write the answers on this sheet.

Name:

Connections

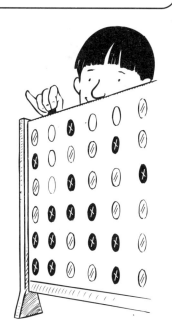

You will need: a pencil and some paper.

DO NOT USE A CALCULATOR

This table shows equivalences between common fractions, decimal fractions and percentages.

- Complete the table.

Common fraction (simplest form)	Decimal fraction	Percentage
$\frac{1}{10}$ ☐ ☐ $\frac{7}{10}$ ☐	0.1 ☐ 0.3 ☐ ☐	10% 20% ☐ ☐ 100%
$\frac{1}{2}$ ☐	☐ 0.25 ☐	☐ ☐ 12.5%
$\frac{1}{3}$ ☐	0.33 recurring ☐	☐ $66\frac{2}{3}$ %

- On a separate piece of paper write down the strategies you used.
  Take this paper to school with this sheet.

- Use the table to help you to find out:

  a the decimal equivalent of $\frac{2}{5}$ ☐

  b the decimal and percentage equivalents of $\frac{3}{4}$ ☐☐

  c the decimal equivalent of $\frac{3}{8}$ ☐

  d the decimal equivalent of 85% ☐

  e $66\frac{2}{3}$% of £300 ☐

  f 20% of £750 ☐

Dear Helper,

Making connections between common fractions, decimals and percentages is very useful in 'real world' applications. When you are out shopping with your child point out any which you notice and ask them to find some. The work on this sheet follows up the mathematics which your child has been studying at school.

Name:

Polyhedra

You will need: a pencil.

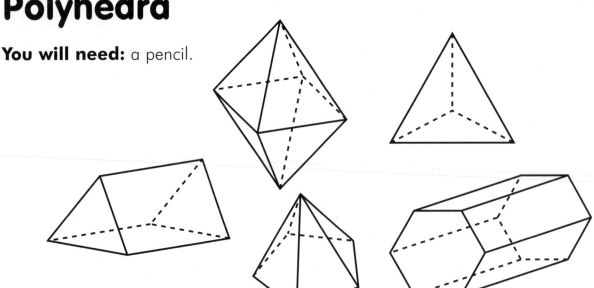

Mr. Topham has been doing shape work with his class and each group has been given a different task. Rob and Kiran's group have been asked to look at the number of faces, vertices and edges that polyhedra have.

Here is their table so far:

Polyhedra	Faces	Vertices	Edges
cube	6	8	12
square pyramid	5	5	8

- Complete the table using the drawings on the sheet to help you.
- Write a brief report of your findings on the back of this sheet.

Dear Helper,

This activity provides your child with the opportunity to look at solid shapes, represented in a 2-D form and also allows them to make a general statement about the relationship between faces, vertices and edges. Encourage your child to take this further and produce a formula in words and possibly letters.

Name:

Pentagons from circles

You will need: a compass, protractor, ruler, some paper and a sharp pencil.

Here is a pentagon constructed from a circle.

- Use your instruments to redraw this diagram next to the one below.

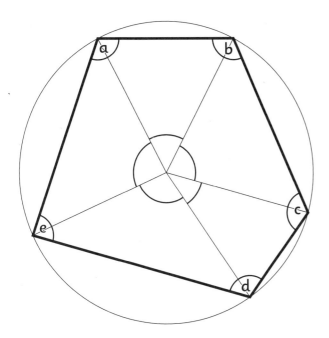

- Now measure each of the angles;

    a _____ **b** _____ **c** _____ **d** _____ **e** _____

- Using the same idea, construct a hexagon of your choice (not regular) on paper and measure its angles.

    a _____ **b** _____ **c** _____ **d** _____ **e** _____ **f** _____

- Find the sum of these angles.

Dear Helper,

In class your child has been constructing regular polygons from circles, this activity extends the idea to any polygon. Your child may need help with their construction and they should be encouraged to estimate the size of each angle before using a protractor.

Name:

Straws and pipe-cleaners

You will need: pipe-cleaners, cut into short lengths of about 2cm, drinking straws, scissors, paper and pencils.

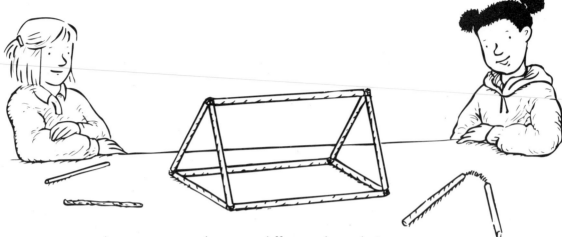

- Use your straws (you may cut them to different lengths) to represent the edges of polyhedra, and pipe-cleaners to join the straws at each vertex, as shown above.

- Work with your Helper and make as many different polyhedra as you can.

- Make a recording chart like this on another sheet of paper:

Number of straws used	Name of shape
9	triangular prism
6	tetrahedron (pyramid with a triangular base)

It might not be possible to make shapes from every number of straws, while with others it is possible to make more than one shape.

What have you found out? _____

_____

Dear Helper,

This activity comes at the end of this term's work on solid shapes and gives an opportunity for your child to organise the way in which the investigation is conducted and draws conclusions from the results obtained. Please ensure that the results are returned with this sheet.

Name:

Shapes using co-ordinates

You will need: graph paper, a ruler and a pencil.

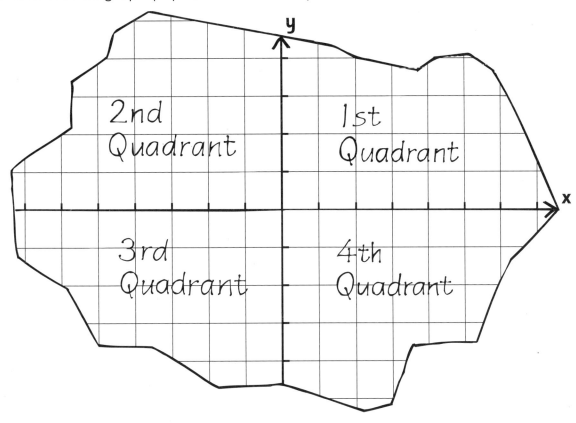

- Draw and label a four-quadrant graph on the graph paper provided.

- On your graph, draw:

    1 a hexagon with co-ordinates (4,9), (8,9), (10,6), (6,–1), (2,–1), (–1,5).

    2 a pentagon with co-ordinates (2,2), (7,1), (11,–5), (3,–6), (–4,–5).

    3 a triangle of your choice, which has two of its vertices in the third quadrant and one in the first.

    What are its co-ordinates? _____

    4 a rectangle which has co-ordinates in all four quadrants.

    What are its co-ordinates? _____

- What do you notice? _____

_____

Dear Helper,

In class your child has been introduced to a four-quadrant graph. This activity gives practice in interpreting and plotting co-ordinates. Your child may still need help with the order in which co-ordinates are read, x value first, followed by y value.

Name:

Co-ordinates - reflections

You will need: graph paper, a ruler and a pencil.

1   Draw and label a four-quadrant graph on the graph paper provided.

2   **a**   Draw a triangle having vertices whose co-ordinates
    are (6,6), (9,10), (11,4).

   b   Reflect the triangle about the:

   (i) 'x' axis and record the co-ordinates

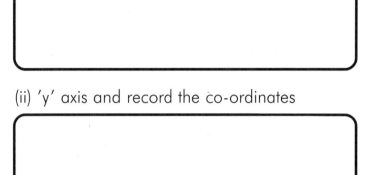

   (ii) 'y' axis and record the co-ordinates

3   **a**   Draw a rectangle having vertices whose co-ordinates
    are (–3,–1), (–1,–3), (–5,–7), (–7,–5).

   b   Reflect the rectangle about the:

   (i) 'x' axis and record the co-ordinates

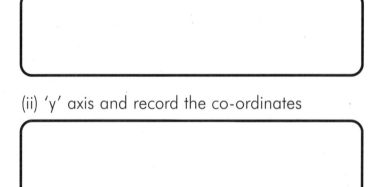

   (ii) 'y' axis and record the co-ordinates

Dear Helper,

Encourage your child to talk to you about reflecting shapes before beginning this homework. If they find the orientation of the reflected shape difficult, a mirror placed along an axis may help. Talk about the strategies they used and any patterns emerging from the co-ordinates.

Name:

Where's the shape?

You will need: a pencil, a protractor and a ruler.

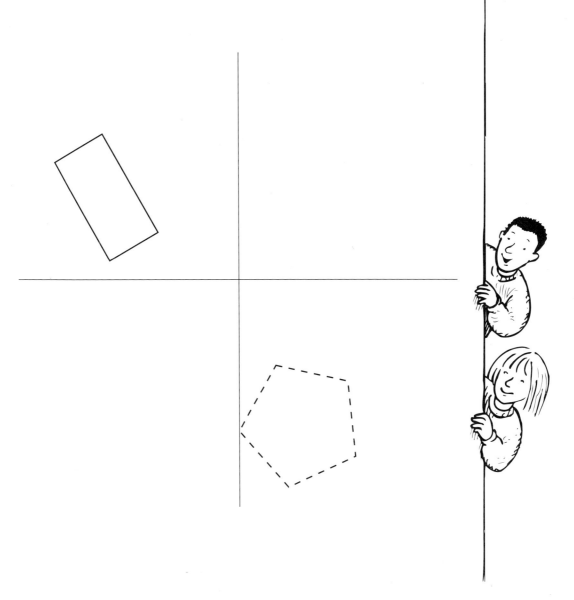

- Reflect the rectangle about the two mirror lines shown and accurately draw the images produced.

- The image shown by the dotted line has been made by reflecting a pentagon in a mirror line touching the shape at a point. Draw the original pentagon in its correct position.

Dear Helper,

Your child has been constructing reflections of shapes in mirror lines which touch the shapes at a point. They have also been using two mirror lines. This activity extends the idea. Your child will need to measure angles and distances accurately, therefore a sharp pencil and accurate use of protractor and ruler will be necessary.

Name:

Areas everywhere

You will need: a pencil, some rough paper, a calculator, a tape measure (at least 3m long) and someone to work with on questions 3 and 4.

1 Finish this sentence:
The area of a rectangle is found by using the formula a = l × b, where a is the area, l the value of the...

_____

_____

2 The area of a table is 11 700cm².
If the length is 130cm, what is the value of the breadth?

_____

3 A living room wall has an area of 7.2m².
Suggest a possible length and height measurement for the wall.

_____

4 Work with your Helper to find some areas of home, for example: your bedroom, the kitchen, the garden. Record your results on the back of this sheet.

Dear Helper,

This homework uses the experiences of working with area which your child has had at school and applies them to the home. Talk through question 3 with them so that a reasonable height is used for the wall. Help them to measure the lengths and breadths required in question 4, using suitable degrees of accuracy. They may also need your advice if the rooms (or garden) are not simple rectangles. Discuss possible approaches with them.

Name:

Puzzling shapes

You will need: a pencil, some thin card (a cereal packet would do), scissors and a ruler.

1 Make a card rectangle like this:

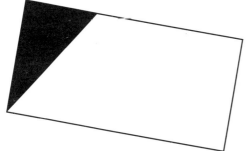

a What was the area of the rectangle?

_____

b What is the area of the parallelogram?

_____

- Cut off the shaded triangle and use the two pieces you are left with to make a parallelogram.

2 This parallelogram could have been made from a rectangle.

- Draw it.

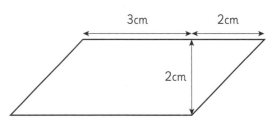

- What is the area of the parallelogram? _____

3 Find the area of this parallelogram.

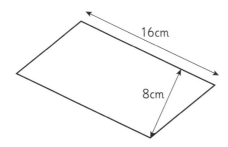

4 Find the area of the shaded triangle.

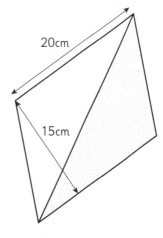

_____   _____

Name:

Which way?

You will need: a pencil, some paper and a calculator.

Remember 1km is about 0.62 miles.

This sketch map shows which places are joined by good roads and the distances between them in kilometres.

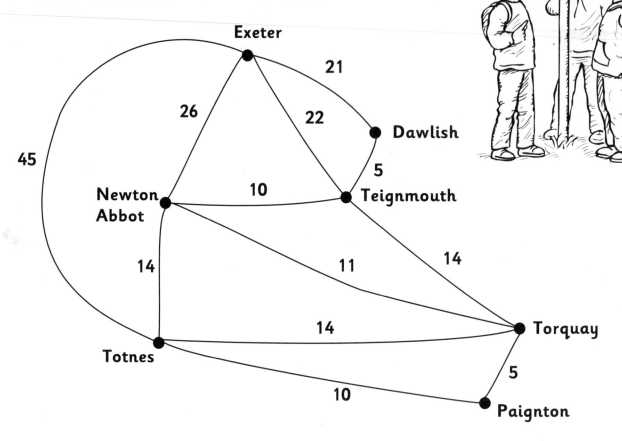

- Is the map drawn to scale? _____

- On a separate sheet of paper draw a map like this showing the distance, to the nearest mile, not kilometre, between places.

- Without visiting any town twice, find and record as many different routes as you can from Exeter to Totnes.

  Work out the distance in miles, the mileage, for each route. Start your recording here.

Dear Helper,

Continue on the back of the sheet.

This investigation gives practice in converting kilometres to miles. The sheet has been designed for your child, but if you would like to try it as well, please feel free!

Name:

Pinball

You will need: some rough paper, a pencil and a calculator.

Jan and Kumar have been playing pinball.
They have had sixteen turns using four balls
for each turn. Here are their scores.

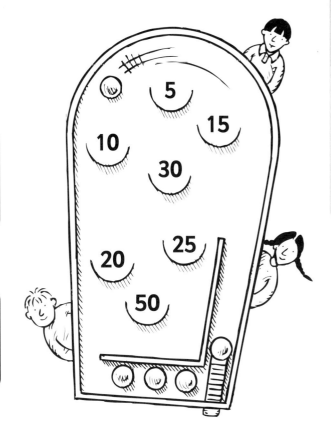

Jan

15, 95, 35, 30, 5, 35, 25, 35,

85, 65, 105, 35, 65, 15, 95, 80.

Kumar

35, 55, 10, 20, 60, 45, 70, 0,

60, 110, 45, 40, 60, 15, 15, 10.

For each set of results find:

a the range
  Jan [   ]   **Kumar** [   ]

b the mode
  Jan [   ]   **Kumar** [   ]

- On a sheet of paper make up some questions about
  the pinball results.

- Try them out on your Helper.

- Write the answers too.

You may now use a calculator to help when you need it.

Dear Helper,

In class your child reviewed aspects of average such as the meaning of mode and range. This activity provides practice in calculating both mode (the result occurring most often) and range (written as the lowest to the highest numbers found). Only use a calculator to help with the answers to your child's questions. If they are stuck you might ask: *Who won and by how many?, 'How many turns had a score over 50? Was finding the mode useful?* Encourage them to think up their own ideas.

Name:

Computer vouchers

You will need: a pencil, some paper and a calculator.

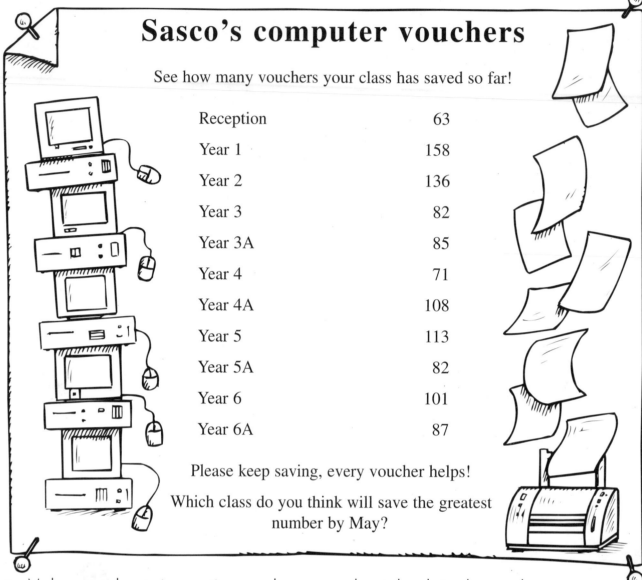

Sasco's computer vouchers

See how many vouchers your class has saved so far!

Reception	63
Year 1	158
Year 2	136
Year 3	82
Year 3A	85
Year 4	71
Year 4A	108
Year 5	113
Year 5A	82
Year 6	101
Year 6A	87

Please keep saving, every voucher helps!

Which class do you think will save the greatest number by May?

- Make up at least six questions and answers about the data shown above. Include questions about range, mode and mean. You may need to use an extra sheet of paper.

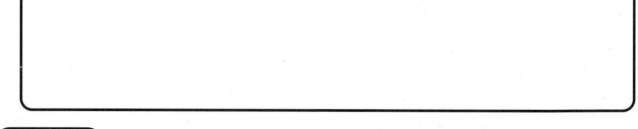

Dear Helper,

Here is an opportunity for the your child to make up their own questions about given data. Encourage them to discuss the uses of the different forms of average.

Name:

Pulse rates

You will need: a pencil, some paper, a calculator and the data concerning the pulse rates of children in the class.

- Use the data you collected to find the average (median and mean) pulse rate for your class.

_____

_____

Is your pulse rate above or below the mean? How much above or below?

_____

- Investigate different pulse rates and record what you find out. For example, you might take your own pulse after you have been swimming, running or hopping, or find out about adult pulse rates.

- Be prepared to tell the class what you find out.

- Write your findings on the back of this sheet or on another piece of paper.

Remember to bring all your work to school.

Dear Helper,

This investigation concludes the work on average for the term. Your child may need help in looking in depth at their data and reporting their findings.

Name:

Guess the graph

You will need: a pencil and paper.

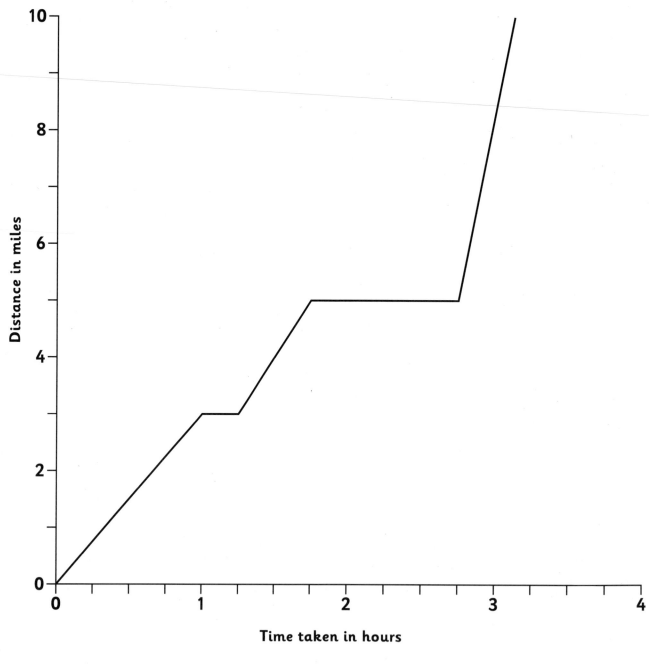

What might this graph represent? _____

On another sheet of paper write all you can about the graph.

Dear Helper,

In class your child has been exploring distance/ time graphs and answering specific questions about the graphs. This homework provides an opportunity for your child to interpret graphs, to make up their own questions and to devise a 'real life' context.

Name:

Repeat it

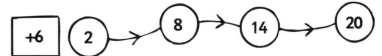

You will need: a pencil, some neat and rough paper. A calculator, if you must!

- Look at these sequences.

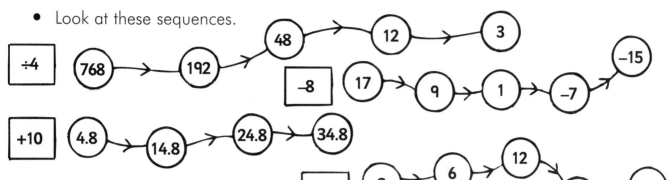

- Now try to puzzle these out.

You may use addition, subtraction, multiplication or division repeating functions.

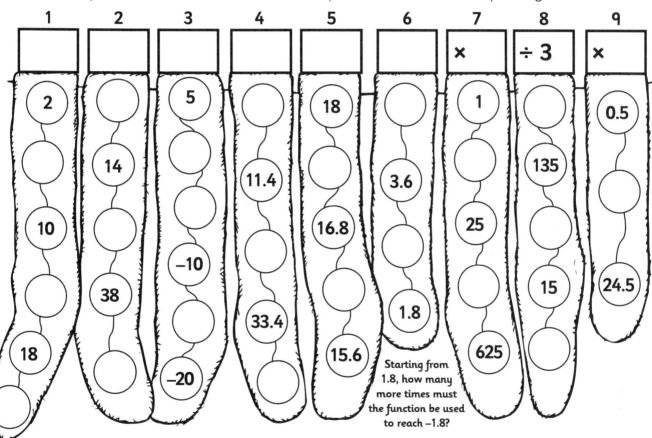

10 a Which function will get you from 15 to 95 in 5 equal steps? _____

    b Which numbers will you visit on the way? _____

- Make up a repeated function question for other children to try.

- Write it on a sheet of paper and bring it to school.

Dear Helper,

At school your child has been exploring repeating functions. This sheet gives further practice. Encourage your child not to use a calculator until they need one. The mental work is really helpful.

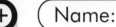
Function fun

You will need: two pencils, some paper, a calculator and someone to work with you and then play the game.

2 Now find the function, or perhaps two functions, for this table and write your answer below.

1 Talk about this table:

Input	Output
3	18
17	32
6	21
10	25
1	16

The function used with the inputs to produce the output was +15.

Input	Output
2	17
6	45
1	10
0	3

- Write in three more inputs, use your function or functions and record the outputs.

3 Play a game of **'Function fun'** with your Helper, using this table to record on.

- First choose a function, or two functions, write it on a sheet of paper, making sure that your Helper cannot see it.

- Ask your Helper to give you an input, write it in the table, use your function and write the output for them.

- Keep playing like this until your Helper thinks that they can tell you the function or functions you chose.

    If they are correct, they score a point.
    If they are incorrect, or cannot solve it, you score a point.
    If you gave a wrong output during the game, your Helper scores the point.

Input	Output

- Draw some more input/output tables and play some more rounds.

- Take turns for who chooses the function or two functions.

- Use the calculator only if the calculations become too difficult.

Dear Helper,

You are needed! By the way, the table at the top right involves two functions (a multiplication followed by an addition is used each time.) Hope you enjoy 'Function fun'.

Name:

Target practice

You will need: a pencil and some rough paper.

You must not use a calculator nor calculate using vertical sums.

Work mentally, but you may jot down any numbers which help. What must you add to each answer to get to the target number?

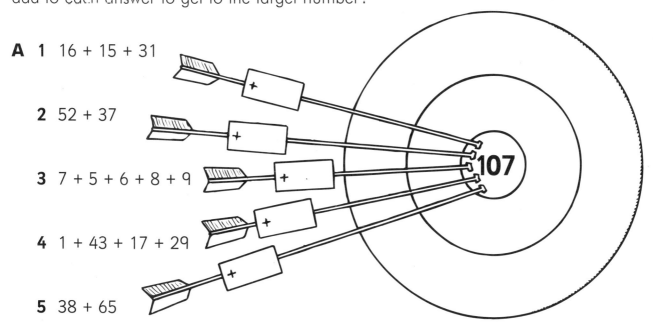

A 1 16 + 15 + 31

2 52 + 37

3 7 + 5 + 6 + 8 + 9

4 1 + 43 + 17 + 29

5 38 + 65

The answers in **B** will include either an + or a – symbol in the boxes.

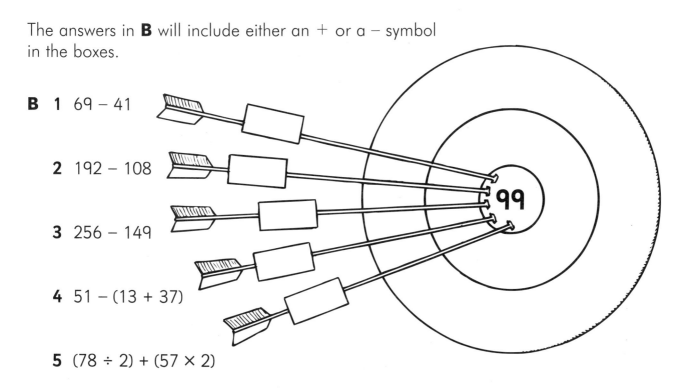

B 1 69 – 41

2 192 – 108

3 256 – 149

4 51 – (13 + 37)

5 (78 ÷ 2) + (57 × 2)

Dear Helper,

These questions give mental practice of addition and subtraction. Please hide the calculator and make sure that your child does not write vertical sums. You might like to discuss the different strategies your child used after they have completed the work.

Name: _____

Midworthy School's Easter Fayre

You will need: a pencil and a calculator.

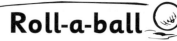

Roll-a-ball

1st prize – book token
2nd prize – basket of fruit
3rd prize – tin of biscuits

Each player had three balls for 'Roll-a-ball'.

Here are the six best scores for the afternoon.

	1st ball	2nd ball	3rd ball	Total score	Prize winners
Miss Bone	500	150	25		
Bob Rouse	125	100	350		
Dave Goss	200	175	400		
Jenny Bates	325	100	375		
Mr Evans	75	450	325		
Jean Sims	250	250	125		

1 Try to work out the answers to this question mentally.

   a Record each person's total score and decide who won which prizes.

   b Wendy ran the stall. 120 people paid 25p each.
      How much did she collect?

_____

   c The book token prize was donated to the stall, the basket of fruit cost £5.35
      and the tin of biscuits £3.90. How much profit did 'Roll-a-ball' make?

_____

2 Here is the money made by the other attractions.

> Bottle stall: 105 people paid 30p each
> Hoop-la stall: 75 people paid 20p each
> Ice-creams: 60p each, 93 sold
>
> Easter egg stall: £53.65
> White elephant stall: £29.17
> Tea and cakes stall: £62.50
>
> Guess the name of the bunny cost 25p a go and 71 people tried.

Use a calculator and its memory keys to calculate the total money earned
by the other attractions listed in question 2. Check your answer.

_____

Dear Helper,

Real-life problems are so important. This sheet encourages mental calculation and the sensible use of
a calculator.

Name:

Conversions

You will need: a pencil and a calculator.

1 The table gives some approximate conversions from ounces to grams.

Use it, with additions or subtractions, to work out about how many grams there are in:

a 3oz **b** 8oz **c** 14oz **d** $1\frac{1}{2}$ lb

ounces (oz)	grams (g)
1	28
2	57
5	142
10	284
16	453

DO NOT USE A CALCULATOR Show your working here:

You may use a calculator for the rest of the questions on this homework sheet.

Check your answers by multiplying.

Check answers **a** _____ **b** _____ **c** _____ **d** _____

Did your checks match the number of grams which you had previously worked out? If not, can you say why? _____

_____

2 Use a calculator to convert these measurements in grams to the nearest ounce.
a 210g _____ **b** 340g _____ **c** 600g _____

3 a Complete this conversion table for length. Check your results by using an inverse operation.

inches (in.)	centimetres (cm)
1	2.54
2	
5	
12	
36	

b How many millimetres are there in:

(i) 7 inches?

(ii) 18 inches?

c Why were 12 inches and 36 inches selected for the table?

_____

_____

Dear Helper,

Since we use both metric and imperial units of measurement, it is important that we can convert from one system to the other. This homework should help.

Name:

Foreign currency

You will need: a pencil, rough paper and a calculator.

The table shows currency rates in six countries around the world.

The currency rate is the amount of local money you will receive for every £1.00 you change.

Country	Currency	Today's rate
USA	US dollar	1.47
Spain	Peseta	269
Greece	Drachma	539.25
Belguim	Belgian franc	64.6
Canada	Canadian dollar	2.15
Austria	Schilling	21.92

The calculations for questions 1 to 3 should be tackled mentally.

1 a Complete this currency rate table which shows pounds to US dollars.

Pounds	US dollars
1	
10	
100	
1 000	

b Draw up a similar table for Canadian dollars.

Pounds	Canadian dollars

2 Mr Jenkins needs £200 in cash for his holiday in the USA. How many dollars will he get for this amount?

3 His brother is off to Canada and wants his £200 to be in Canadian dollars. How many Canadian dollars will he receive?

4 Six months ago the exchange rate for Spanish currency was 252 pesetas to the pound.

a What would the difference be in pesetas if £350 was exchanged today compared with six months ago?

b How much is the difference worth in pounds at today's rate?

5 In Greek shops, a Zolex 203 camera costs 175 200 drachmas. In Belgium the same camera costs 19 800 Belgian francs, and in Austria it costs 7 560 schillings. In Great Britain, the camera costs £315. Which country's shops are offering the camera at the lowest price? You may use a calculator.

Dear Helper,

At school your child has been converting pounds to foreign currency. This homework gives more practice of this activity. Assume 'today's rate' is given in the table on this page. Please make sure that a calculator is used only for question 5.

Name:

Factors and primes

You will need: a pencil, some scrap paper and a calculator.

1 Which number less than 50, has the greatest number of factors?

_____

2 a Which of these numbers has an odd number of factors?

16   49   76   121   129   169   225

_____

b Can you say why?

_____

_____

A prime number is a number which is divisible only by itself and 1 (these two numbers must be different).

3 Is 1 a prime number?

_____

4 Find and write down all the prime numbers to 120.

Dear Helper,

These activities revise and build on work which your child has done at school. Talk to your child about the strategies they are using. For example, in question 2, pairing factors helps. 16. 1 × 16, 2 × 8, 4 × 4. 5 factors altogether 1, 2, 4, 8 and 16. An odd number of factors.

100 MATHS HOMEWORK ACTIVITIES • YEAR 6 TERM 2

PHOTOCOPIABLE

95

Factorising and prime factors

You will need: a pencil and some scrap paper.

For each of the numbers below 'yes' has been written if they are prime numbers and 'no' if they are not.

Unfortunately some mistakes have been made.

1 a Can you find and correct them?

Number	Is it prime?	Factors
21	no	
23	yes	
25	~~yes~~ no	
27	yes	
29	yes	
31	yes	
33	no	
35	yes	

b Write in each number's factors, in the third column.

2 a 24 can be factorised as 12 × 2 or 4 × 3 × 2. Find two other ways.

_____

_____

Find two ways of factorising:

b 28 [ ]

c 45 [ ]

d 54 [ ]

e 76 [ ]

A prime factor is a factor which is a prime number.

3 Find the numbers less than 20 which can be factorised using prime factors only.

Number	4	6
Prime factors	2 × 2	2 × 3

Dear Helper,

These questions give practice in finding prime numbers, for example 19, 37. They also find factors, for example the factors of 16 are 1, 2, 4, 8, 16. Numbers are factorised, 27 is written as 9 × 3 or 3 × 3 × 3, and finally numbers are factorised using prime factors only. For example, 12 as 3 × 2 × 2, as both 3 and 2 are prime numbers. Let your child try the questions by themselves, but be ready to give help if it is needed.

NUMBER PROPERTIES   NUMBERS AND THE NUMBER SYSTEM

PHOTOCOPIABLE

100 MATHS HOMEWORK ACTIVITIES • YEAR 6 TERM 2

Big wheel

You will need: a pencil, neat paper and scrap paper.

- Find the central number.

- Find a number for each box to complete the 'Big wheel'.

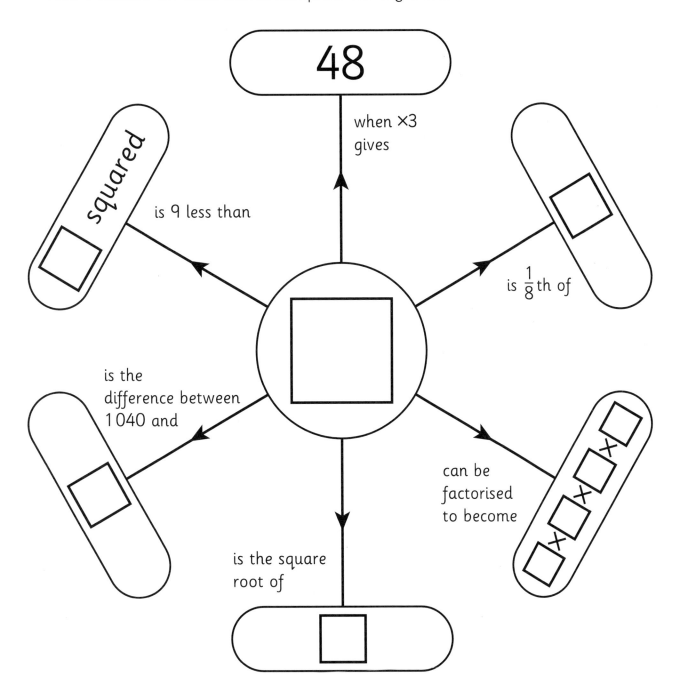

- Invent a 'Big wheel' puzzle of your own and bring it to school for your friends to try.

Dear Helper,

Make sure that your child fills in all the box answers. Encourage them to include challenging statements on their Big wheel. You may like to help them produce it. Make sure that their wheel is as neat as possible. Hide the calculator.

Pathways

You will need: a pencil and some paper.

Here are some functions for you to use mentally in the Pathways puzzle below.

- Use one function in each of the circles.
  You must use each function at least once.

- Write the results in the oblongs which follow.

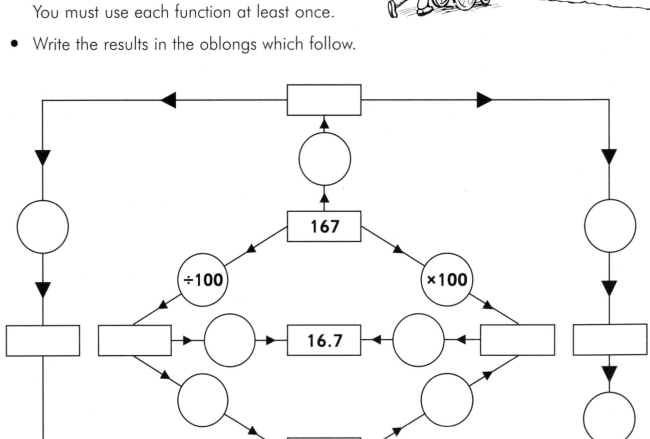

- Make up a different pathway network to be used with the same six functions.

- Solve your puzzle and bring it to school.

Dear Helper,

Hide the calculator. You may wish to help your child create the new network.

Name:

Make it real

You will need: a pencil, some paper and a calculator.

Write your answers to question 1 on a separate piece of paper.

1 Think up a 'real life' situation where each of these numbers might be found.

a 4 506   **b** 17 358   **c** 115 000

d 1 500 000   **e** 0.16   **f** 0.05

• Now write 'real life' situations for these sets of numbers.

a	**b**	**c**	**d**
10.03	40.3	28.3 seconds	23 462
10.21	47.2	29.0 seconds	10 229
10.37	38.9	28.6 seconds	8 416
10.42		28.4 seconds	

Total: 114.3

Average: **28.6 seconds**

2 Use a calculator to find the answers to these questions, rounding each to the nearest tenth. Record your answers in the boxes.

a $114 \div 9 =$ ☐   **b** $1476 \div 13 =$ ☐   **c** $26.4 \times 17.2 =$ ☐

3 Round to the nearest whole number.

a $15.3 \times 18 =$ ☐   **b** $27.36 \times 38 =$ ☐   **c** $253 \div 52 =$ ☐

4 Choose one of the calculations in question 3 and suggest a 'real life' reason for rounding it to the nearest whole number.

Dear Helper,

At school your child has been using numerical information in 'real life' contexts, including rounding numbers to the nearest tenth or whole number. When this sheet has been completed you might like to discuss your child's answers to questions 1 and 4.

Name:

Multi-hex

You will need: a pencil and some paper.

Do not use a calculator for this homework.

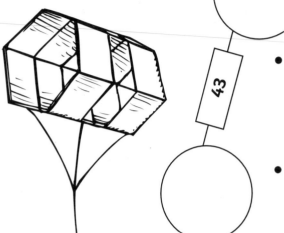

16

25

43

19

17

34

- Write a number in each circle equal to the product of the numbers in the oblongs on either side of it.

- Use paper for your working out and remember to bring it to school with this homework.

- In the same way, make some rhombus puzzles like this on a sheet of paper. Write two-digit numbers in the oblongs for your friend to find the circle products.

Make sure you know the answers.

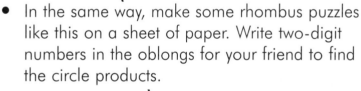

Dear Helper,

In class your child has been using their own methods to solve longer multiplications. This homework gives them the opportunity to practise these methods. Encourage them to explain their written methods to you and make sure that the calculator is kept out of the way.

Name:

What's the cost?

You will need: a pencil and paper.

Mrs Jacks wants to arrange a trip to the newly-opened Aquarium. She made enquiries and here are the details she noted:

ACME COACH £56·50 (48 SEATER)

ENTRANCE FEE £1·36 CHILDREN £3·20 ADULT

LUNCH £2·26

64 children and 8 parents, including Mrs Jacks, have said that they want to go.

37 want the available packed lunch, while the remainder will provide their own.

Acme Coaches have said that each passenger need only pay £1.45.

Mrs Jacks must collect all the money before the trip.

How much must she collect?

How generous was Acme Coaches?

- Use a sheet of paper, or the back of this sheet, to work out the answers and do not use a calculator. Remember to bring all your working to school.

Dear Helper,

This homework gives your child the opportunity to use their arithmetic skills to solve a 'real life' problem. Encourage them to read the information carefully.

Name:

Timed divisions

You will need: a pencil, paper, a stop-watch, a calculator and a Helper to time you.

- Ask your Helper to time you with these division calculations.

  Do not use your calculator yet.

- Try each set.

- Work out your calculations on another sheet of paper and write your answers by the side of the questions on this sheet.

- Write down your times for each set.

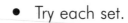

Set 1

a $414 \div 18 =$

b $884 \div 26 =$

c $893 \div 19 =$

d $1085 \div 31 =$

Time taken:

Set 2

a $608 \div 16 =$

b $782 \div 46 =$

c $972 \div 36 =$

d $1272 \div 53 =$

Time
taken

Now use your calculator to check your answers.

Dear Helper,

Long division calculations have been introduced in the lesson and some children will be using an expanded written method whilst others will be secure with a shortened form. Encourage your child to discuss their working and written presentation before using the calculator to check.

Exploring numbers

You will need: a pencil, rough paper and a calculator.

- Write down three consecutive numbers, for example: 3, 4, 5.
- Now multiply the first and third number together ($3 \times 5 = 15$)
- Square the middle number ($4^2 = 16$)

What do you notice?

Try other sets of consecutive numbers does it always work?

- What if the difference between the numbers is 2, for example, 2, 4, 6?

- What about other numbers like 7, 17, 27 (difference 10) or 4, 9, 14 (difference 5)?

Try large numbers using the calculator to help and don't forget decimals.

Use another sheet of paper to write a report of your findings.

Dear Helper,

The questions on this sheet are intended to encourage your child to explore numbers in depth. It will be helpful if you could discuss their findings.

Name:

Getting close

You will need: a pencil.

You will not need a calculator for this homework.

- Ask your Helper to time you for each question and to write down the time taken by the side.

1 In the table below, the estimates (whole numbers only) have been muddled.

- Write the correct estimates in the column provided.

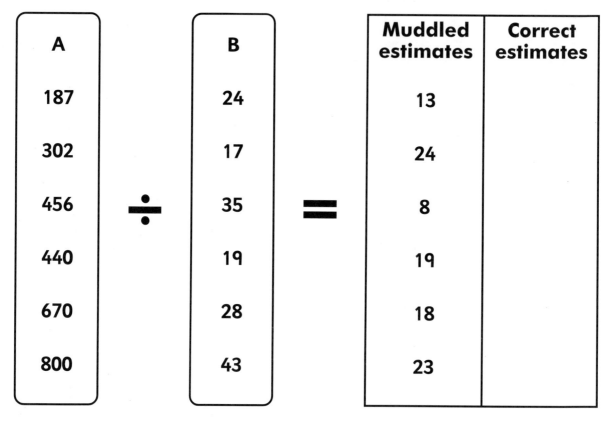

A		B		Muddled estimates	Correct estimates
187		24		13	
302		17		24	
456	÷	35	=	8	
440		19		19	
670		28		18	
800		43		23	

2 Write your estimates to these divisions, getting as close as you can, (whole numbers only).

a 319 ÷ 18

b 193 ÷ 16

c 206 ÷ 24

d 354 ÷ 25

e 284 ÷ 19

f 171 ÷ 27

Dear Helper,

In class your child has been playing a game involving mentally estimating the division of a three-digit number by a two-digit number. This homework continues this theme and involves an understanding of the relationships between all four operations. Encourage your child to discuss their strategies with you.

Name:

Mixed and matched

You will need: a pencil and some rough paper.

DO NOT USE A CALCULATOR

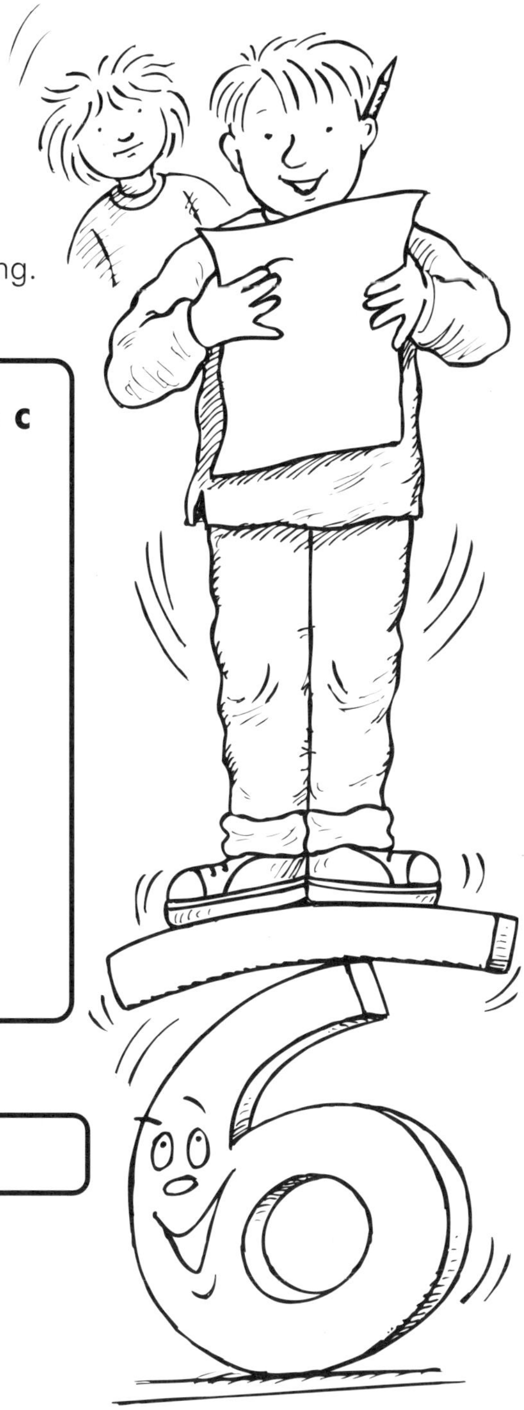

- Find the partners. Write your answers in the oblong.

  One has been done for you.

1 $\frac{15}{4}$ a $6\frac{1}{8}$

2 $\frac{17}{9}$ b $4\frac{2}{3}$ | **1 with c** |

3 $\frac{72}{16}$ c $3\frac{3}{4}$

4 $\frac{14}{3}$ d $4\frac{1}{3}$

5 $\frac{26}{6}$ e $1\frac{8}{9}$

6 $\frac{49}{8}$ f $4\frac{1}{2}$

7 What's the difference between:

  a c and f? [ ]   **b** d and e? [ ]

  c f and d? [ ]

8 Which of these fractions is nearest to 5?

  $\frac{48}{8}$ $\frac{17}{3}$ $\frac{11}{2}$ $\frac{75}{16}$ $\frac{29}{6}$ [ ]

9 Finish these statements:

  a 40 is [ ] times bigger than $\frac{4}{10}$

  b $\frac{4}{28}$ in its simplest form is [ ]

  c [ ] in its simplest form is $\frac{5}{6}$ and is $\frac{1}{4}$ of [ ]

Dear Helper,

Work in school involving mixed numbers, for example, $3\frac{1}{5}$, $7\frac{1}{8}$, and fractions in their simplest form, for example, $\frac{2}{6}$ is $\frac{1}{3}$, is practised here. A calculator is not needed.

Name:

Triangular growth

You will need: a sharp pencil and a ruler.

● Complete these statements:

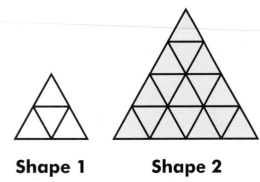

Shape 1   **Shape 2**

1 a there is 1 small triangle in shape 1 for every ⬜ in shape 2.

b Shape 1 has a ⬜ of the area of shape 2.

2 What is the ratio of white to shaded triangles?

3 What proportion of the total number of triangles is shaded?

_____

4 On the triangular grid draw a triangle with length of side **6cm**. How many small triangles are enclosed in it?

_____

5 What is the ratio of small triangles;
a in shape 1 to those in shape 3?

_____

b in shape 2 to those in shape 3?

_____

6 If you drew an equilateral triangle with length of side **8cm**, what would be the ratio of small triangles in shape 1 to those in this shape?

_____

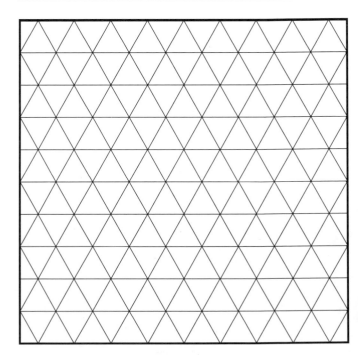

Shape 3

Dear Helper,   ● Check your answer by drawing the triangle.

Ratio which compares part to part, for example 'two to every five' and proportion, 'two in every seven', feature in these activities. This follows up the work your child has been doing in school. Only help if your child asks. Please make sure that their pencil is sharp.

Name:

Using percentage

You will need: a pencil and some rough paper.

- Try these without using a calculator.

1 a 75% of £2000

b 80% of £15.00

c 16% of £10.00

d 25% of 10kg

e 30% of 5km

f 12.5% of 80cl

2 At Bransford Restaurant, 42% of those dining were women, 34% were men, 12% were girls, the rest were boys.

a What percentage were boys? _____

b If the total number of people dining was 50, how many were:

(i) female? [   ]   (ii) male? [   ]

3 A pair of trousers which normally cost £30 at Hansons, were in the sale with a 20% discount. Mrs Seymour bought the trousers and gave the cashier £40. How much change did she receive?

_____

4 In a class maths test, the children who sit at Serena's table scored the following marks out of 50: Serena 43, James 38, Jesse 31, Vince 29.

a Write each mark as a percentage.

Serena [   ]   James [   ]   Jesse [   ]   Vince [   ]

b Which of the children scored more than $\frac{3}{4}$ of the possible marks? _____

c At William's table his percentage was 92%, whilst Wesley scored 84%, Maria 66% and Roberta 54%. How many marks out of 50 did each score?

William [   ]   Wesley [   ]   Maria [   ]   Roberta [   ]

Dear Helper,

A calculator should not be used but a piece of rough paper may be useful for jotting down intermediate steps in the calculations. The questions follow up work on percentages at school.

Name:

Timing TV

You will need: a pencil, a calculator and a TV programme guide.

Here is the data from a survey showing the amount of time given to various types of programme on BBC 1 between 6.00pm and 10.30pm on a particular evening:

Type of programme	Number of minutes	Approximate % of viewing time
News	90	33%
Comedy	30	
History	50	
Quiz	35	
Holiday	25	
Drama	40	

- Finish the table, rounding each percentage to the nearest whole number. Use a calculator and don't forget the percentage key.

- Carry out your own 6.00pm to 10.30pm survey for BBC 2 or ITV programming, using the programmes shown for any evening this week. You decide the type of programme breakdown and titles.

Dear Helper,

This investigation links percentages, which your child has been studying at school, with a survey. Help may be needed with choosing the names of programme categories, such as soaps, natural history, cooking or current affairs.

Netball results

You will need: a sharp pencil, some paper, a protractor and a calculator.

1 Lynside Primary School netball team has played 12 matches this year. The pie chart, when completed, will show the number of matches won, lost and drawn, represented as a percentage of the matches played.

● Complete the pie chart.

Pie chart showing _____

_____

Won 8 **66.66%**

Lost _____

Drawn _____

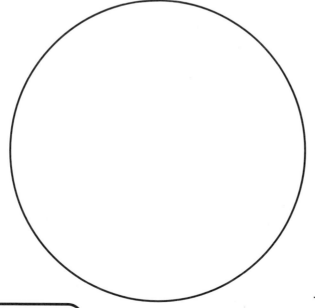

2 Henwick Primary School played 12, won 6, lost 4 and drew two games.

● Work out the results as percentages of the 12 games played and show all the information on a pie chart.

● Draw it in the space below.

Pie chart showing _____

_____

Dear Helper,

Pie charts are often used to represent percentages graphically. Encourage your child to draw the pie chart accurately and label it neatly. You may not be needed but be ready to offer support if necessary.

PHOTOCOPIABLE

Decigrid

You will need: a pencil and some rough paper.

DO NOT USE A CALCULATOR

1 Find the decimal equivalents of these common fractions.

Use rough paper for any calculations you need.

a $\frac{1}{8}$ = 0.125 $\qquad$ $\frac{1}{4}$ = [ ] $\qquad$ $\frac{3}{8}$ = [ ] $\qquad$ $\frac{1}{2}$ = [ ]

$\frac{5}{8}$ = [ ] $\qquad$ $\frac{7}{8}$ = [ ]

b [$\frac{1}{5}$] = 0.2 $\qquad$ $\frac{2}{5}$ = [ ] $\qquad$ $\frac{3}{5}$ = [ ] $\qquad$ $\frac{4}{5}$ = [ ]

c [$\frac{1}{10}$] = 0.1 $\qquad$ $\frac{3}{10}$ = [ ] $\qquad$ $\frac{7}{10}$ = [ ] $\qquad$ $\frac{9}{10}$ = [ ]

2 Solve the 'Decigrid' puzzle.

a Each number can be found by adding or subtracting two of the decimal equivalents you found in question 1. Two have been completed for you.

0.95	0.75	0.2	0.15
0.75 +0.2			
0.575	0.075	1.15	1.2
0.725	1.4	0.025	0.975
		0.625 −0.6	
0.4	0.7	1	0.775

b Find the difference between the sum of the 2nd row and the sum of the 2nd column.

[ ]

c Show that half of the sum of the 2nd row is $\frac{7}{8}$ less than the sum of the 3rd column.

[ ]

Work the answers out on rough paper and write them in the spaces above.

Dear Helper,

These activities follow up the work on common fractions and their equivalent decimals which your child has done at school. Please give help if your child asks and do not allow them to use the calculator.

Name:

Stepping stones again

You will need: two cubic dice, some paper and a pencil.

Mr Hall's class want to play the 'Stepping stones' game they played in class, and Tom has suggested that instead of adding the numbers on the two dice, the class should multiply them together.

1 Which numbers will it be possible to make?

2 If you were playing, on which stones would you place your seven counters (no more than three on one stone) and why?

3 What do you think about Tom's idea?

Dear Helper,

Playing the game of 'Stepping stones' has helped the your child to appreciate ideas of probability. Encourage your child to talk about the game and their strategies for placing pieces.

Name:

Graphs from ordered pairs

You will need: a pencil.

1 Find the value of y in the equation **x + y = 7** when x has the value:

a 5 ⬜   **b** −5 ⬜   **c** 10 ⬜

d 12 ⬜   **e** −2 ⬜   **f** −11 ⬜

2 Find the ordered pairs (x,y) for **x + y = 9**. Use values of x from −5 to 5.

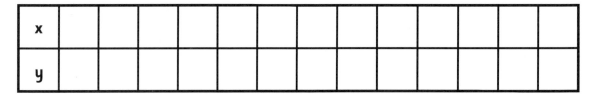

x											
y											

3 Draw a graph to show the ordered pairs for **y = 6 + x**, for values of x from −4 to 8. Write your set of ordered pairs here before you draw the graph and remember to label both axes.

x												
y												

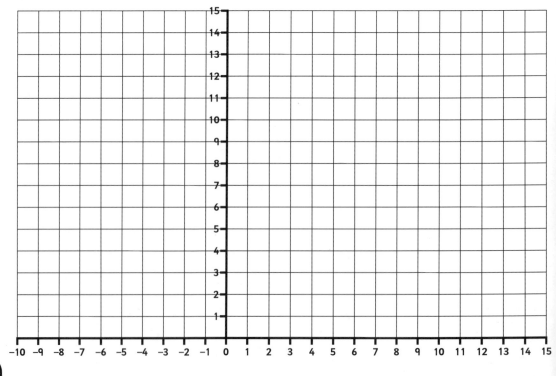

Dear Helper,

Your child has been drawing line graphs using four quadrants. Encourage them to talk to you about the ordered pairs (x and y co-ordinates) of say, x + y = 10.

Name:

Name that graph!

You will need: a pencil, calculator and rough paper.

Use rough paper for any working you need to do, but
remember to bring it to school with this homework.

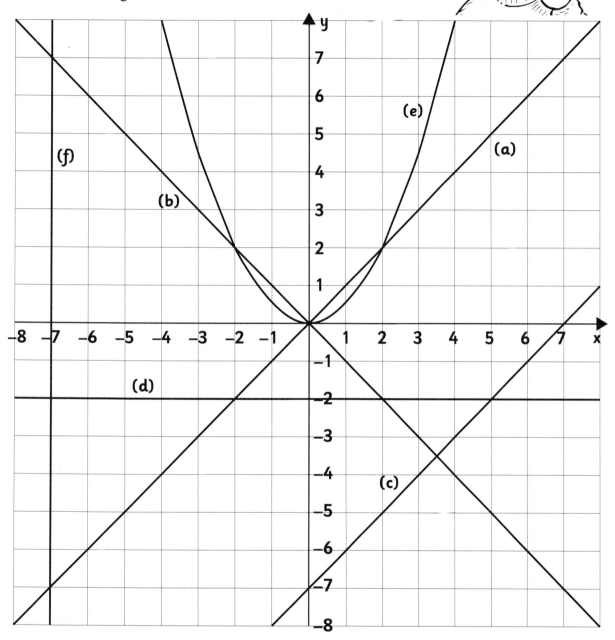

What are the equations of the lines drawn on the graph above?

a	b	c

d	e	f

Dear Helper,

This homework draws together the term's graphical work. Talk to your child about the strategies they used
for identifying each of the equations they have graphed.

SOLVING PROBLEMS

REASONING ABOUT SHAPES

Name:

Find the triangles

You will need: a pencil, some rough paper, a protractor and a ruler.

- Draw a regular pentagon with sides measuring 3cm.

- Now draw any three of its diagonals.

- Work out a method for finding all the triangles in your pentagon.
  Use rough paper for sketching your ideas.

  How many triangles are there? Record your method.

Dear Helper,

This activity gives your child the opportunity to draw accurately and to employ strategies to solve a problem. Encourage your child to discuss their ideas for finding a solution and perhaps offer some yourself.

Name:

Where is it now?

You will need: a pencil, some rough paper, a protractor and a ruler.

Each of these shapes has been rotated about one of its vertices and an image drawn.

1 Show which vertex has been used and find the angle of rotation of each shape. Don't forget to say if it is clockwise or anti-clockwise.

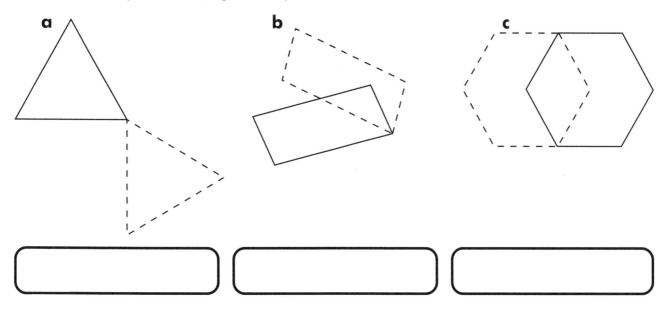

a   b   c

2 Draw a triangle having two edges of 3cm, one of 4cm and an angle of 50°.

• Choose one vertex and rotate the triangle through 90°.

• Accurately draw the image of the triangle after it has been rotated. You may choose to rotate the triangle clockwise or anti-clockwise.

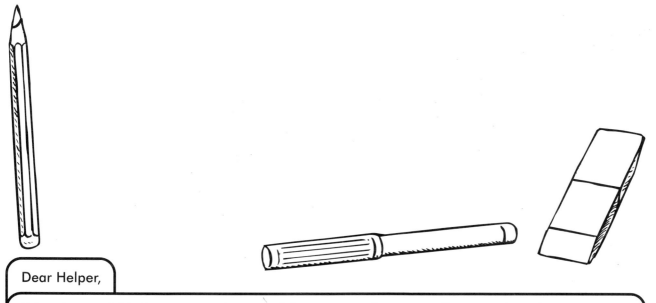

Dear Helper,

Talk with your child about moving shapes and the meaning of rotation, reflection and translation. Encourage them to estimate the angle of each rotation in question 1 and to predict the position of the image to be drawn in question 2.

Name:

Following instructions

You will need: a pencil, some rough paper, tracing paper, two different coloured pencils or felt-tipped pens, a protractor and a ruler.

Follow these instructions carefully:

- Draw a simple shape near the left edge of your sheet of paper.

- Colour in this shape.

- Now mark a point near your shape, call it A.

- Rotate your shape 180° about A, use tracing paper to help you.

- Mark a point B near your new image.

- Rotate the image 180° about B.

- Use another colour to colour this new image.

Is there a way of producing the final image without using a rotation?

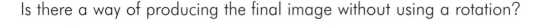

Dear Helper,

Your child will need to follow each instruction carefully to produce the final image. It may be helpful to read and discuss each instruction with them and to encourage the use of rough paper before producing a final drawing on this sheet.

How does it get there?

You will need: a pencil.

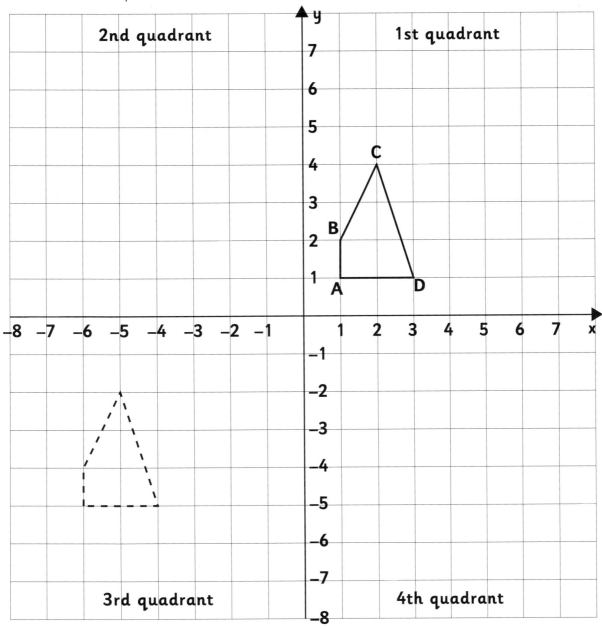

The drawing above shows a quadrilateral ABCD which has been translated twice and its image drawn.

- Describe how ABCD has been translated.

Dear Helper,

There are two possible solutions to this homework problem. Encourage your child to consider both possible translations; from first to second to third, and then trying from fourth to third.

Name:

Counting diagonals

You will need: a pencil, compasses, a ruler and some rough paper.

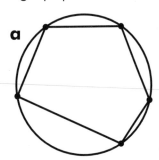
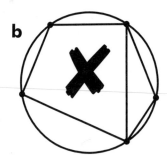

Diagram **a** shows five points drawn on a circle and joined.

Is it possible to draw any more straight lines joining the points, without making any triangles? Diagram **b** would not be allowed because the joining line makes a triangle.

- Use rough paper and try this with other numbers of points drawn on a circle. Record your results in the table below.

Number of points	1	2	3	4	5	6	7	8	9	10	11	12	13	14	15	16	17	18
Number of lines drawn																		

Are you able to predict the number of lines drawn on a shape with **25** points?

- Write all that you notice about your results?
  Use this sheet and continue on a separate sheet of paper if necessary.

Dear Helper,

It is important that your child can put mathematical findings into words. Here is an opportunity for them to express their initial findings and discuss with you, before producing a written report.

Name:

Tug o' war

You will need: a pencil, some rough paper and a calculator.

Each year Kyford and Evalmoor tug o' war teams have a match.

Here are the weights of the members of each team given to the nearest kilogram.

Kyford   Evalmoor

1 For each team find: Kyford   Evalmoor

    a the total weight

    b the mean

    c the median

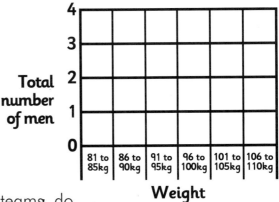

    d Which team do you think stands the best chance of winning? Why?

---

2 Fill in this frequency table combining the data from the two teams.

	81 to 85kg	86 to 90kg	91 to 95kg	96 to 100kg	101 to 105kg	106 to 110kg
Kyford	0					
Evalmoor	1					
Total number of men	1					

3 Draw a bar chart from the grouped data in the frequency table.

Total number of men

4
3
2
1
0

81 to 85kg | 86 to 90kg | 91 to 95kg | 96 to 100kg | 101 to 105kg | 106 to 110kg

Weight

4 If we had information from other tug o' war teams, do you think that men with a weight of between 96kg and 105kg would always have the highest frequency? Why?

Dear Helper,

At school your child has been combining work on measures with data handling, and this homework gives further practice of this. Discuss some of the questions, particularly 1d) and 4, with your child.

119

MEASURES   MEASURES, SHAPE AND SPACE

Name:

Cora's 100cm² puzzle

You will need: a sharp pencil, some paper, an envelope, a ruler and scissors.

• Carefully cut out each of the triangles below.

• Arrange the triangles to form a square with an area of 100cm².

• Can you invent a puzzle, which uses six triangles, arranged to form a square with an area of 400cm²?

Carefully draw the square on an A4 piece of paper and divide it up with lines to form six triangles inside.

Carefully cut out your six triangles and put them in an envelope.

Bring your puzzle to school for other children to solve.

Dear Helper,

This activity follows up work on area which your child has been doing at school. If they find the puzzle difficult, ask: *What is the length of side of a 100cm² square?* Measuring the lengths of the sides of the triangles will also help. Make sure that your child writes their name on the envelope.

Name:

Around the world

You will need: a pencil, a world map and a telephone directory.

Ask your Helper to work with you.

- Use the world map together with the international codes section of the telephone directory to find a country, or part of a country, for each of the hours shown on the Time Zone line.

  Some are shown to get you started.

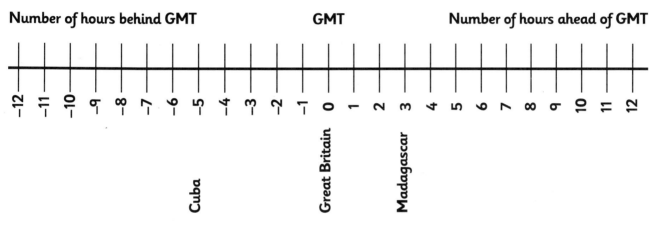

Number of hours behind GMT   GMT   Number of hours ahead of GMT

-12 -11 -10 -9 -8 -7 -6 -5 -4 -3 -2 -1 0 1 2 3 4 5 6 7 8 9 10 11 12

Cuba   Great Britain   Madagascar

- Write down any interesting facts which came out of your investigation.

Dear Helper,

You should be able to find a suitable world map in an atlas. The international codes section of the Phone Book shows differences from Greenwich Mean Time (GMT) for the countries listed throughout the world. You may not have planned a round the world trip for this year, but maybe one day...

SOLVING PROBLEMS · NUMBER PROBLEMS IN MONEY

Converting measures

You will need: a pencil, a ruler and a calculator when needed.

1 Use the pounds/kilograms conversion line, to find how many pounds there are in a kilogram.

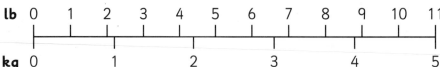

lb 0   1   2   3   4   5   6   7   8   9   10   11

kg 0   1   2   3   4   5

2 One parcel weighs 0.5kg and another 3.5kg.

a Mark these weights on the line and write down the equivalent values in pounds.

b Use the line to find the total weight of the parcels in pounds. Check your answer by calculation.

This conversion graph relates gallons and litres.

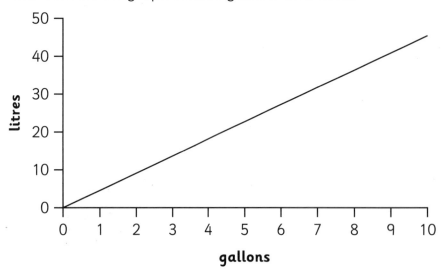

3 About how many litres are there in a gallon?

4 Simeon says 4 gallons is about 18 litres. Show this on the graph and check by calculation.

5 About how many gallons are there in 30 litres? Show this on the graph.

6 If petrol costs 82p a litre, how much is petrol a gallon?

7 Mr Trowesdale used 32 litres of petrol in a week and Mrs Symes 9 gallons. Who used the most and by how much? Give your answer in litres.

Dear Helper,

Your child has been solving problems involving measurement conversion at school, including the use of graphs. These activities give further practice in this.

Name:

Target basketball

You will need: a pencil, neat paper and rough paper.

You must not use a calculator.

- Mentally add, subtract, multiply or divide any of the five ball numbers to make the basket numbers.

- Each time use as many of the ball numbers as you like.

- Jot down any steps along the way on rough paper.

- Record every calculation for each number on a separate piece of paper and bring it to school.

- Ask your Helper to check your work.

Score 2 points for each 'basket score'. What was your total?

Dear Helper,

This is a mental activity, but jottings on rough paper can be recorded. Your child should not use a calculator, but you can use one for checking if you wish.

Name:

Trouble-shooting

You will need: a pencil and a calculator

Please can you help? A mistake has been made on each invoice.

• Find the mistake and write the correct invoice.

Correct invoice.

Production details	Quantity	Cost per item inc VAT	Total
Bloomsgrove Settee	1	554.00	554.00
Bloomsgrove Chairs	2	216.54	433.80
		TOTAL	987.80

er item AT	Total
0	
4	
TOTAL	

Vehicle Carina E Reg. L970 ADV	
Repair details	**Total**
Touch up bonnet and near-side wing.	39.50
Paint near-side top corner of bumper.	48.35
Total excluding VAT	87.85
VAT at 17.5%	16.25
TOTAL DUE	104.10

DV	
	Total
ing.	
per.	
Total excluding VAT	
VAT at 17.5%	
TOTAL DUE	

LIVE WIRE Electrical Supply		Total
To supply and install 3 bells and transformer and necessary wiring.		
	Materials	68.32
	Labour	67.50
	Total excluding VAT	135.82
	Discount at 15%	13.58
	Total with discount	122.24
	VAT at 17.5%	21.39
	TOTAL DUE	143.63

	Total
Materials	
Labour	
Total excluding VAT	
Discount at 15%	
Total with discount	
VAT at 17.5%	
TOTAL DUE	

Dear Helper,

At school your child has been solving invoice questions using a calculator. The invoices have included discounts and VAT. Please provide help only if it is needed.

Crack it!

You will need: a pencil, neat paper and rough paper.

Here is Georgia working on her code.

She has used two functions, one followed by another, to make the code.

Can you crack it?

.... so **b** is 4.

.... so **e** is 13

.... so **j** is 28

.... so **m** is 37

Here is the alphabet laid out to help you. Complete the code number row.

	a	b	c	d	e	f	g	h	i	j	k	l	m
Number order	1	2	3	4	5	6	7	8	9	10	11	12	13
Code number		4			13					28			37

Functions used

[ ] followed by [ ]

	n	o	p	q	r	s	t	u	v	w	x	y	z
Number order	14	15	16	17	18	19	20	21	22	23	24	25	26
Code number													

- Make up a message using Georgia's code on a separate sheet of paper.

- Bring it to school for others to try to crack the code.

Dear Helper,

Codes are always fun. This homework follows up the code work your child has done at school. You might like to try to crack Georgia's code yourself on a separate piece of paper - no cheating! Work with your child if they find cracking codes difficult.

Name:

Multiple problems

You will need: a pencil.

DO NOT USE A CALCULATOR

Here is a Venn diagram which is not finished.

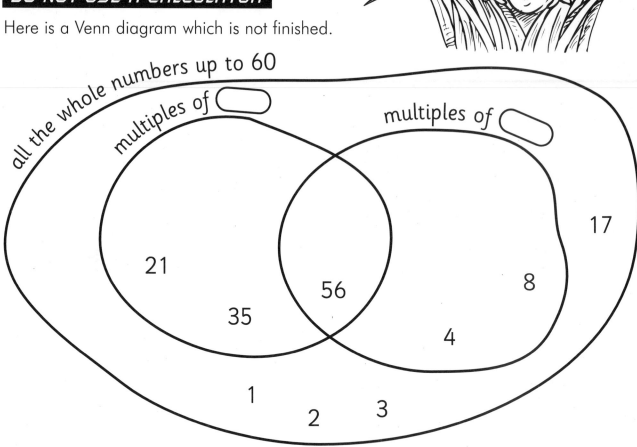

all the whole numbers up to 60

multiples of ⬭

multiples of ⬭

21

35

56

17

8

4

1

2

3

1 a Work out what it is showing and complete it.

　　b Use the diagram to help you complete this sentence.

　　The lowest common multiple of ☐ and ☐ is ☐.

2 a Find four common multiples of 2 and 6 which are less than 30.

_____

　　b Find two common multiples of 5 and 7 which are greater than 40.

_____

　　c What is the lowest common multiple of 3, 8 and 9?

_____

Dear Helper,

Venn diagrams have been used at school in order to represent common multiples of two numbers, as shown above. Calculators are not allowed.

what can you say?

You will need: a pencil and some paper.

Investigate each of these numbers using
square number, triangular number,
multiple and prime number properties.

- Write down all you find out on a separate
  piece of paper and bring it to school.

- Here are three examples to get you started:

    4 is a square number; the sum of two adjacent triangular numbers,
    1 and 3; and is a multiple of 1, 2 and 4.

      13 is the sum of two square numbers; and is prime.

        20 is the sum of two square numbers, 4 and 16; the sum of
        four triangular numbers 1, 3, 6 and 10; and is a multiple of 1,
        2, 4, 5, 10 and 20.

Dear Helper,

All of the number properties mentioned above have been explored during this school year. This
pulls the ideas together. Work with your child if they you would like you to.

Name:

What's the difference?

You will need: a pencil, some paper and a calculator.

Here are the first ten square numbers with some differences recorded.

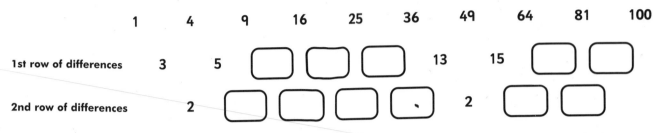

	1	4	9	16	25	36	49	64	81	100
1st row of differences		3	5	☐	☐	☐	13	15	☐	☐
2nd row of differences			2	☐	☐	☐	☐	2	☐	☐

1 Complete the table of differences and write down what you found out.

_____

_____

2 **a** Write down the sequence of numbers to 200 which is produced when each square number is doubled. Space them out as shown in the table above.

b Complete the table of differences for this sequence.

c What happened this time?

_____

3 **a** On a separate piece of paper, try using cubic numbers, up to 10^3 (1 000), and finding three rows of differences instead of two. Use a calculator to help you.

b What happened with this set of numbers? Say exactly what occurred.

_____

...vestigate what would happen if you doubled or trebled the ...bic numbers and developed a difference pattern.

...umbers were developed in your child's lessons at school. Cubic numbers have ...example, three cubed (3^3) is $3 \times 3 \times 3$ (27). The difference patterns here may ...g.

homework